Basics of English

READING
and
VOCABULARY

Lee C. Deighton

 **HARCOURT BRACE JOVANOVICH, INC.**
New York / San Diego / Chicago / San Francisco / Atlanta

Basics of English Series:

Grammar and Usage

Spelling

Reading and Vocabulary

HBJ Center for Lifelong Education

Printed in the United States of America

Library of Congress Catalog Card Number: 79-65410

ISBN: 0-15-505152-0

ACKNOWLEDGMENTS

For permission to reprint copyrighted material, grateful acknowledgment is made to the following sources:

JOAN DAVES: Excerpts from *In the Deserts of This Earth* by Uwe George. Copyright © 1976 by Hoffmann Und Campe Verlag. English translation copyright © 1977 by Harcourt Brace Jovanovich, Inc. By permission of Joan Daves.

HARCOURT BRACE JOVANOVICH, INC: Excerpts from: *America: Its People and Values* by Ralph H. Gabriel and Leonard C. West. Copyright © 1975 by Harcourt Brace Jovanovich, Inc. *American Business: An Introduction* by Ferdinand F. Mauser and David J. Schwartz. Copyright © 1978 by Harcourt Brace Jovanovich, Inc. *Consumer Choice: The Economics of Personal Living* by Andrew J. Allentuck and Gordon E. Bivens. Copyright © 1977 by Harcourt Brace Jovanovich, Inc. *In the Deserts of This Earth* by Uwe George. Copyright © 1977 by Harcourt Brace Jovanovich, Inc. *The Prodigious Builders* by Bernard Rudofsky. Copyright © 1977 by Harcourt Brace Jovanovich, Inc.

HUMAN NATURE Magazine: Excerpts from "Anxiety" by Jeffrey A. Gray; "Baseball Magic" by George Gmelch; "The Medical Power of Faith" by Jerome D. Frank. Reprinted by permission of *Human Nature* Magazine, copyright © 1978, Human Nature, Inc.

MARTIN SECKER & WARBURG LIMITED: Excerpts from *The Prodigious Builders* by Bernard Rudofsky.

Contents

Introduction   1

Lesson 1. Words Have Many Meanings   3

2. How Words Get New Meanings   11

3. How Your Vocabularies Grow   17

4. The Meaning That Fits   25

5. Check Your Progress   34

6. The Writer's Signals   40

7. Connectors   48

8. Clues from Sentence Structure   56

9. Words Work Together   61

10. Check Your Progress   66

11. Prefixes   72

12. Prefixes with More Than One Meaning   78

13. The Main Job of Suffixes   84

14. Facing Up to Long Words   89

15. Check Your Progress   97

Midway Check   103

Lesson 16. Words Don't Always Mean What They Say   111

17. Literal and Figurative Language   119

18. Suggested Meaning   125

19. Seeing the Writer's Purpose   130

20. Reading Newspaper Headlines   135
21. Check Your Progress   142
22. What Is the Next Sentence
        Doing?   149
23. More About the Next Sentence   154
24. Reading the News Story   158
25. Watch the Details   164
26. Practical Reading   167

Final Test   172

Key   179

Introduction

A good shortstop can make a tough play look so easy that you wonder why he gets paid for it. A good mechanic can make a repair without seeming to try. Some cooks can turn out a great meal quickly, simply, and without any fuss. How do these people do it?

Well, there are tricks to any trade, and the tricks make the job easier. It not only *looks* easier; it really *is* easier. It's the same way with reading.

A good reader can turn through a newspaper in fifteen minutes without missing a thing. He reads quickly, gets the meaning, and remembers it. He knows what to look for and how to size up what the words are saying. There are tricks to reading well. This book will show you many of them.

The ability to read well is not just a single skill. It is a whole group of skills that work together. Like everyone else, you are better at some of these skills than at others. You can sharpen all of your skills, and when you do, reading will be easier. You will be able to get more meaning in a shorter time.

This is a book, then, about reading. But the title is *Reading and Vocabulary*. Why vocabulary? What has that to do with reading?

Vocabulary has to do with words and their meanings. You have to know what the words mean to make your reading profitable. You don't always need an exact meaning for a word, but you do need a reasonable idea of what it is about.

There are ways to figure out word meanings without going to the dictionary. This book will show you how.

Make this book work for you. Read the first part of each lesson carefully. Then try your hand at the practice materials. Here you can put to work what you have read and make it yours for good. As you go along, you will find yourself reading more easily and with much greater understanding.

There is a Key at the end of the book. Use it to check your answers. If your answer does not agree with the Key, take the time to figure out where you went wrong. If you do this, you will be much less likely to make the same mistake twice. But use the Key *after* you have gone through the practice.

Lesson 1. Words Have Many Meanings

Exact meaning is very important to doctors, lawyers, and scientists. They can't afford to use words that wobble—words that mean one thing here and something else there. They prefer to use technical terms when they can, because these terms do not carry old meanings with them. When something new comes along, new terms are invented—such as *quark*, *quasar*, and *laser*—with only one meaning assigned to them.

But even scientists do not always succeed in pinning down one word to one meaning. Recently the word *charm* was used to name the attraction of one sort of particle to another. There was objection at once, because *charm* in ordinary affairs has several meanings that have nothing to do with particles. And of course, scientists cannot avoid some words, such as *field*, *force*, *nucleus*, and *atom*, that have been used a long time in ordinary affairs.

Some words in common use, such as *telephone*, *typewriter*, and *airplane*, have only one meaning. This is also true of the names of many instruments: *piano*, *T square*, *scalpel*, *computer*.

But most of the words in common use have more than one meaning. This may seem too obvious a fact to mention. Yet readers often become confused because they put the wrong meaning on a word. They assume that words are always used with the same familiar meanings.

It seems to be true that most of us have one or two meanings in mind for common words. We are apt to associate a word with its most frequent use. The word *stop*, for example, appears so often as a traffic signal that we usually think of it as meaning "halt, cease motion." But *stop* also has some twenty other meanings, such as:

1. to close by filling, shutting off, or covering

    to plug up a hole
    to block up a pipe
    to close a bottle with a cap or cork

3

2. to keep something from starting or happening

   to prevent a proposed action
   to ask the bank to withhold payment on a check
   to break up a play

3. to stay for a while

   to visit a place or person

4. to discontinue

   to hold up delivery of mail
   to cancel a subscription

The simple word *and* provides another example. Most of us think of it as meaning "also, in addition." But it may also mean "as a result" or "in contrast."

   He took the wrong turn *and* was lost for an hour. (result)
   She said she would come *and* she didn't. (contrast)

Try substituting "also" for *and* in these sentences, and (result) you will see that it does not fit.

How serious is this variety of meanings in a simple word? Well, for *run*, there are more than 100 meanings. For *with*, one dictionary lists more than forty meanings. Even for *tongue*, there are eleven different meanings. The editors of dictionaries have a problem in listing so many meanings. They sometimes solve the problem by grouping meanings that are closely related, that have a common idea. Thus, one large dictionary arranges the meanings of *take* in twenty-five groups, each with a common idea. Among the common ideas are:

to get possession of	(to *take* a city)
to pick out	(to *take* your choice)
to make use of	(to *take* your time)
to make, do, or perform	(to *take* a walk)

4

The editors of dictionaries have their problems; the rest of us have a different sort. We have to choose, from the many meanings of a word, the one meaning that fits what we are reading. We cannot assume that any word always has one of the meanings we are most used to.

CHECK IT OUT

A. Which statement comes nearest to the ideas stated in the passage above? Place an *x* on the line next to your choice.

1. The fact that words have many meanings is important only to dictionary editors. _____

2. Readers must remember that a writer may be using an unfamiliar meaning for a common word. _____

3. Scientists always make up new words, such as *quasar* and *quark*, to name new discoveries. _____

4. All of the words in common use have more than one meaning. _____

5. The meanings of all common words can be put into groups that have a common idea. _____

SOLVE THE WORD PUZZLES

B. Which of the following words probably have only one meaning? Write *yes* or *no* on the line provided.

1. blue _____   **6.** error _____

2. calipers _____   **7.** appendicitis _____

3. program _____   **8.** stay _____

4. electrode _____   **9.** move _____

5. carburetor _____   **10.** dictate _____

C. Which of the following words from science and mathematics have other meanings in everyday language? Write *yes* or *no*.

1. circle   _____   **6.** decimal   _____

2. liter   _____   **7.** electron   _____

3. gravity   _____   **8.** solution   _____

4. wave   _____   **9.** magnet   _____

5. nucleus   _____   **10.** methane   _____

D. In each pair of sentences, the same word is *italicized*. Decide whether its meaning is the same in both sentences. Write *same* or *different*. The first one is done for you.

1. As the delay in repairing the streets went on, a *wave* of annoyance swept over the city.
   There was a *wave* of relief across the country when the spacecraft landed safely.   _____*same*_____

2. We have had no *word* from the travelers.
   No *word* of what was happening came from the White House.   _____

3. I'll *match* you to see who pays for the beers.
   Palmer lost the *match* on the eighteenth hole.   _____

4. I can't listen to the radio *while* I am studying.
   While we like Figuera, we don't have real confidence in him.   _____

5. This pass will *admit* you to the plant.
   Jack's policy was never to *admit* anything.   _____

6. The police car *passed* us with all sirens going.
   The town was dark when we *passed* through.   _____

7. How did you *learn* that we need money?
   Helen signed up to *learn* stenotyping.   _____

8. Somehow the secret *leaked* out.
One of the guards *leaked* the committee's decision to the
newspapers. _____

9. Did you *watch* TV last night?
You have to *watch* what you say to her. _____

10. We were not at home *last* evening.
Dick split enough wood to *last* through the winter. _____

E. Two common ideas are given for each word. Below them the
word is used in five sentences. Decide which idea applies to
each sentence. Write its letter on the line provided. The first
one is done for you.

about   (a) concerning
          (b) close to

1. We know all *about* that.   _a_

2. It is *about* six o'clock.   ____

3. What is the quarrel *about*?   ____

4. The job is just *about* finished.   ____

5. He is some place *about*.   ____

with   (a) in the company of
         (b) because of

6. The man was charged *with* arson.   ____

7. They were green *with* envy.   ____

8. She is no longer *with* the team.   ____

9. The tools come *with* the car.   ____

10. She is very sick *with* the flu.   ____

turn   (a) move in a circular manner
           (b) change

11. They *turned* the chair to face the light.   ———

12. The cider *turned* to vinegar.   ———

13. The earth once *turned* more rapidly than it does now.   ———

14. His tears quickly *turned* to laughter.   ———

15. The cream *turned* sour overnight.   ———

trust   (a) confidence in
           (b) duty or task

16. You will have to *trust* her judgment.   ———

17. We put our *trust* in his honesty.   ———

18. Being a parent imposes a *trust*.   ———

19. The purity of our water supply is a public *trust*.   ———

20. We give credit to our customers on *trust* that the bills will be paid.   ———

take   (a) make use of something
           (b) to lay hold of something

21. We will *take* the smaller car.   ———

22. You can *take* this road right into town.   ———

23. Why did he *take* you by the arm?   ———

24. *Take* the basket by the handles.   ———

25. Let's *take* the time to do it right.   ———

Odd Expressions

If we stop to think about some of the things we say, they sound very strange and sometimes very funny.

A man may say, "Wait a moment until I *light my pipe*." He then makes a match burst into flame and holds the flame over the tobacco in the bowl of the pipe. As he draws on the pipestem, the flame comes in contact with the tobacco and starts it burning. Smoke now comes out of the bowl and stem, but there is no light. The pipe is as dark as before, but the man says it is lighted.

It would have been more accurate to say, "Wait until I start my tobacco burning."

Sometimes we use shortcuts. For example, we may say, "Rita's Diner is a good place to eat." We don't really mean that the chairs have a good flavor, or that the roof is tender, or that the windows are crisp and crunchy. We really mean that Rita's Diner is a good place *in which* to eat. Saying "a good place to eat" is a shortcut; we leave out the words that would make the statement sensible.

One of our funniest expressions, when you think about it, is "catch a cold." The original meaning of *catch* was "to seize and hold." You can catch a pig or catch a ball, but how do you seize and hold a cold? A cold is an inflammation of the mucous membranes in the nose, throat, and sinuses. But there is nothing *cold* about it. In fact, sometimes a person with a cold feels hot from a fever.

We may never know why this inflammation was named a *cold*. There may be a very reasonable explanation. But most people would agree that the expression *to catch a cold* is a funny combination of ideas. Still, it is easier to say than "incur an inflammation of the mucous membranes."

F. The word *take* has a great many different meanings. Several of them may be grouped under the following common ideas. Decide which common idea applies in each phrase below. Write the letter of the common idea. The first one is done for you.

(a) to get by force or skill
(b) to get from a source
(c) to make use of
(d) to undergo or endure

1. to win (take the championship)   _a_

2. to borrow (take a line from the Bible)   ____

3. to occupy (take a chair)   ____

4. to capture (take the fort by storm)   ____

5. to derive (take his mother's name)   ____

6. to benefit from (take exercise)   ____

7. to seize (take the criminal in the act)   ____

8. to put up with (to take the bad with the good)____

9. to do something with (take the opportunity)   ____

10. to submit (take a beating)   ____

Lesson 2. How Words Get New Meanings

Let's imagine a bit of history. Overnight a strange object appeared in the middle of a Chicago street. No one saw it come. No one knew how it got there. It was ten feet in height and forty feet around. It made no sound; it gave off no odor. But there it was with a rough, shiny surface.

The first persons to see it stopped to look, but as others gathered, rumors began. *It's a UFO. It's a publicity stunt. It's the Russians. It's a bomb.* The crowd became uneasy and drew back. Police roped off the area, and a bomb squad arrived. Scientists from the university came to test it. At length, they issued a report saying that the object seemed to be a rock made of a very hard substance, slightly radioactive. People said with relief, "Oh, it's only a rock." The evening papers called it "The Chicago Rock," and everyone felt better about it, although the mystery remained.

Whenever something new occurs or is created, it must be given a name so that we can talk about it. We take great comfort in names. Once a thing is named, it loses some of its mystery and terror.

Scientists usually invent names for their discoveries so that the new things will not be confused with anything else, but even scientists sometimes give up. After inventing *quark* and *quasar* they came upon objects in the sky that baffled them. They simply called these objects "black holes."

In everyday affairs we usually employ a familiar word to name something new, because this is easier than inventing a new term. But this naming is not haphazard. Something in the new object or event reminds us of something we already know—its size, shape, use, or the material of which it is made. We apply the name of the familiar thing to the new situation. This is the usual way in which words gather new meanings.

The history of some words is quite clear and easy to follow. They seem to have moved from one meaning to another in a straight line. See how directly the meanings of *board* developed:

11

1. a long flat piece of wood (a plank)
2. a flat piece of wood used for a special purpose (a chessboard, a bulletin board, an ironing board)
3. a flat piece of any material used for construction (fiberboard, pasteboard)
4. a flat piece of wood used as a table for meals (a board laden with food)
5. food served on such a table
6. a table around which members of a council sit
7. a group of persons who control or manage something (board of directors, board of education)

Another group of meanings grew from the fact that ships were first made from boards. The side of a ship came to be called a board (*on board, overboard*). We now speak of *boarding* a bus or airplane, both of which are made of metal!

For other words, the history is not easy to follow. The meaning may take a sharp sudden turn with no relation to what has gone before. Thus, *against* first meant "in opposition to." Somehow, it later came to mean "next to, adjoining" and "in contact with" as in *leaning against the fence.*

So also, *with* first meant "against" as in *argue with your friends.* Later, it meant exactly the opposite: "to support," as in *I'm with you.*

One more example: the basic idea of *blast* is "a strong rush of air." You can follow this idea through one meaning after another. But suddenly, without warning, you find that *blast* may also refer to a blight or disease of a plant.

In dealing with words, keep in mind these sudden reversals and turns in meaning.

CHECK IT OUT

A. All of the following statements agree with the passage you have just read. One statement best sums up the whole passage. Find this statement and place an *x* on the line next to it.

12

1. We take great comfort in names.   _____

2. It is easier to use a familiar word than to invent one in order to name something new.   _____

3. We do not give new meanings to old words in a haphazard way.   _____

4. It is usually easy to see how one meaning of a word developed from an earlier meaning, but sometimes there is a turn in meaning that is not related to what has gone before.   _____

5. We often apply the name of something familiar to a new object or event because the new thing reminds us of something we are familiar with.   _____

TRY IT OUT

B. Several meanings are given for each **keyword** in heavy black type. Decide which meaning the keyword has in each sentence. Write the number of the correct meaning. The first one is done for you.

Keyword	*Meanings*
1. land	(1) to arrive at a certain place
	(2) to leave a ship or plane
	(3) to succeed in getting something

a. The passengers will *land* in Boston.   _2_

b. Maria hopes to *land* a job at the bank.   _____

c. His hat *landed* in the mud.   _____

d. We will *land* part of the cargo tonight.   _____

e. If you jump from here, you will *land* in the grass.   _____

13

Keyword	Meanings
2. late	(1) tardy
	(2) far into a period of time
	(3) having recently died
	(4) most recent

a. The *late* Dr. Gomez was admired by everyone.   ____

b. *Late* in the season, the women's basketball team began winning. ____

c. Because of a flat tire, we were *late* to work.   ____

d. Showers began *late* in the afternoon.   ____

e. She always wears the *latest* styles.   ____

Keyword	Meanings
3. mark	(1) target
	(2) a sign of something
	(3) pay attention to
	(4) a starting line

a. The shortstop's throw was way off the *mark*.   ____

b. Listening carefully to someone is a *mark* of courtesy.   ____

c. The arrows fell short of the *mark*.   ____

d. *Mark* these words well.   ____

e. Jesse Owens was very quick getting off the *mark*.   ____

Keyword	Meanings
4. model	(1) a small copy of something
	(2) worthy of imitation
	(3) to wear clothing in order to display it
	(4) style or design

a. Sue's hobby is building *model* airplanes.   ____

b. Jim's courage was a *model* for the rest of the team. _____

c. A *model* of the proposed building is on display. _____

d. Beth will *model* in the junior style show. _____

e. The new car *models* are shorter and lighter. _____

C. The same italicized word occurs in each group of sentences. In two sentences, it has the same meaning. In the third, the meaning of the word is different. Find this sentence and place an **x** on the line next to it. The first one is done for you.

1. (a) The lemonade is not *sweet* enough. _____

   (b) I like *sweet* butter better than salted. _**x**_

   (c) Pete has a craving for *sweet* foods. _____

2. (a) Two of the eggs in the carton were *broken*. _____

   (b) The tie was *broken* in the last of the ninth. _____

   (c) Rain was pouring in through the *broken* window. _____

3. (a) The package was *bound* with silk thread. _____

   (b) His arms were *bound* behind his back. _____

   (c) You are *bound* to forget all those numbers. _____

4. (a) A raging fire *swept* across the prairies. _____

   (b) A rumor *swept* through the crowd. _____

   (c) Julie *swept* the snow off the steps. _____

5. (a) This writer has a peculiar *brand* of humor. _____

   (b) Try this new *brand* of peanut butter. _____

   (c) He picked up a burning *brand* from the fire and threw it at the animal. _____

6. (a) *Watch* the magician's hands closely. ____

   (b) Are you going to *watch* the tennis match? ____

   (c) Your *watch* seems to be slow. ____

7. (a) Wait until I catch my *breath*. ____

   (b) There was not the slightest *breath* of suspicion about the treasurer's accounts. ____

   (c) Figuera had the *breath* knocked out of him. ____

8. (a) That was not a very *bright* remark. ____

   (b) There are three very *bright* women in the class. ____

   (c) We were dazzled by the *bright* lights. ____

9. (a) The band played a lively *air*. ____

   (b) The fresh *air* will wake you up. ____

   (c) The *air* in the room was stale. ____

10. (a) This victory ought to *build* up their confidence. ____

   (b) The developers plan to *build* six houses here. ____

   (c) Judy is trying to *build* up her strength. ____

Lesson 3.   How Your Vocabularies Grow

You have four different kinds of vocabularies (vo•cab′u•lar•ies). One is your *speaking* vocabulary, the words you use in everyday talk at home or at work. Another is your *writing* vocabulary, the words you use in notes, letters, reports, or any other kind of writing you do. It is somewhat larger because you have time to stop and find the right word. Your *listening* vocabulary is still larger. It consists of words that you understand, more or less, when you hear them. Many of these words you would never use in speaking or writing.

Your *reading* vocabulary is the largest. It consists of all the words you recognize when you see them. You may not know the exact meaning of all of them. You may not know how to pronounce some of them, but you have an idea of what they mean.

A vocabulary, then, consists of words *and* meanings. As your vocabularies grow, two things happen:

1. you add new words
2. you add new meanings to familiar words.

Your vocabularies don't stand still. They continue to grow as long as you have new experiences. You meet new words in your studies, in newspapers, and on radio and TV programs. Of course, you have to do more than just meet them.

You can get wet without any effort just by standing in the rain. The rain does all the work. But to improve your vocabularies, you do have to make an effort. Just what do you have to do?

You might take some authority's list of important words and try to learn a meaning for ten new words a day. This is not a very good method. For one thing, most words have more than one meaning; for another, the normal human rate of forgetting is very fast. By the end of a week, the words and meanings of the first day would be fading. Within ten months you would have forgotten most of what you had memorized.

You learn about words through repeated experience with them. You acquire meanings gradually. The first time you meet a word, you figure out what seems to be its meaning. The second time, you get a bit more meaning, and this goes on until you can use the word yourself with confidence. Then, suddenly, the word appears with a different meaning, and you start over again. You don't throw away the old meaning; you add the new meaning to it.

You never get all of a word's meanings at any one time, simply because a word can have only one meaning in a particular sentence. Let's see how this works.

A few years ago, baseball rules were changed so that a player could be sent in to bat for a weak hitter without removing that player from the game. Each team was allowed to carry a set number of players whose only job was to bat. They were called *designated batters*.

Now you know something about a *designated batter*. He can take a turn at bat and walk back to the bench without having to field, pitch, or catch when his team goes back onto the field. But what about the word *designated*? Read through these sentences:

1. The old house was *designated* as an historic building.
2. Mr. Renaldo has been *designated* as the mayor's representative in Washington.
3. Every day three ferry boats meet at a *designated* spot on the river.
4. Three of the worn-out buses were *designated* to be junked.

With a little effort you can figure out that *designated* means "marked, named, or specified." Your meaning for the word becomes surer each time you see it.

What is the effort, then, that you must make to improve your vocabularies? It is very simple: you have to give your attention to new words and new meanings and try to figure out what they refer to.

CHECK IT OUT

A. According to the passage you have just read, which of the following statements are correct? Write *true* or *false*.

1. Your vocabularies grow without your doing anything about them just so long as you keep having new experiences. _____

2. The best way to improve your vocabularies is to memorize a few words every day. _____

3. A vocabulary consists of words and meanings. _____

4. You never learn all the meanings of a word in one meeting with it. _____

5. You can learn the meanings of a word very quickly. _____

6. Vocabulary growth requires giving attention to words and trying to figure out their meanings. _____

Note: Up to this point you have been working with plain, ordinary words that you already know something about. But this is not enough. You need to know how to deal with words that are new to you. To give you this power, we will have to use some words that you probably don't know. Don't be afraid of them. The text and the work will help you deal with them easily.

TRY THESE

B. The italicized word has the **same** meaning in each of the three sentences. What is that meaning? Three answers appear below each group of three sentences, but only one is right. Place an *x* on the line next to the correct meaning. It must fit in all three sentences. The first one is done for you.

1. *canceled*
   The bank *canceled* the check by stamping it on the face and on the back.
   The wavy lines through the stamp show that it has been *canceled*.
   The store manager *canceled* the coupon by writing his name across it.
   (a) destroyed _____

   (b) marked to prevent further use ___*x*___

   (c) refused to accept _____

19

2. *ambiguous*

The doctor's report was so *ambiguous* that Carlos didn't know whether he would get well or not.

The Senator's reply was *ambiguous*; we didn't know whether he would vote for the bill or against it.

The *ambiguous* directions could have meant for us to turn either to the right or to the left.

(a) having more than one possible meaning   ——

(b) difficult   ——

(c) not true to the facts   ——

3. *arrogant*

The mayor made an *arrogant* reply, saying that he would decide what was best for the town by himself.

The clerk had an *arrogant* manner with the customers, acting as though they were interrupting her work.

The women disliked the *arrogant* way in which the supervisor put down their suggestions and ignored their complaints.

(a) overbearing   ——

(b) stupid   ——

(c) unfriendly   ——

4. *bolstered*

The Pirates *bolstered* their attack by signing two heavy hitters.

The case for the defense was *bolstered* by new evidence.

The old bridge was *bolstered* by adding new steel girders.

(a) repaired   ——

(b) changed   ——

(c) strengthened   ——

5. *brazen*

The owners shut down the plant in *brazen* defiance of the court.

The commissioner's reply was a *brazen* denial of the facts.
The increase in repair charges was a *brazen* attempt to fleece the public.

(a) shameless ____

(b) illegal ____

(c) false ____

6. *capricious*

Jerry's choice of a secretary was *capricious* since he knew nothing about the girl's ability.
We objected to the *capricious* firing of the two men who had worked hard for the company for years.
The decision to move the office seems *capricious*, for everyone likes the present location.

(a) well thought out ____

(b) acting suddenly without clear reasons ____

(c) unfriendly ____

7. *commonplace*

The reviewers praised the program loudly, but it seemed *commonplace* to us.
We had expected an exciting account from the explorer and were disappointed in his *commonplace* remarks.
A college education was unusual among our parents but is *commonplace* today.

(a) ordinary ____

(b) desirable ____

(c) extraordinary ____

8. *bland*

After a while his smooth, *bland* manner became tiresome.

You will find this medicine very *bland*.
Plain custard is too *bland* for my taste.

(a) agreeable   _____

(b) calm   _____

(c) mild   _____

9. *calculate*

The statement was *calculated* to mislead us.
He made a *calculated* effort to win new friends.
The budget was *calculated* to win our support.

(a) estimated   _____

(b) reduced   _____

(c) planned   _____

10. *diverted*

By using bags of sand and hastily dug ditches, the men *diverted* the stream from its channel.
The overturned trailer blocked the highway, and traffic was *diverted* to side roads.
The front doors were closed and the crowd was *diverted* to the rear entrance.

(a) stopped   _____

(b) turned away   _____

(c) prohibited   _____

C. Watch for the turn in meaning. The meaning of the italicized word is the same in two sentences in each group. In one of the three sentences, it is different. Find this sentence and place an *x* on the line next to it.

1. (a) His *face* was smeared with grease. _____

(b) A smile lit up her *face*. _____

(c) The *face* of the building is made of limestone. _____

2. (a) Who will *care* for the garden while you are gone? _____

(b) I don't *care* for sugar, thank you. _____

(c) My mother takes *care* of the children when I am at work. _____

3. (a) Did you see the football *game* on TV last night? _____

(b) She hunted big *game* in Africa. _____

(c) You can have six or seven players in the *game* of hearts. _____

4. (a) The early school teachers would *lodge* with the families in the area. _____

(b) The beaver *lodge* is at the end of the pond. _____

(c) Iroquois *lodges*, called "long houses," were built of wood. _____

5. (a) Storm sewers *carry* off the rain and melted snow. _____

(b) These wires *carry* electricity into the buildings. _____

(c) Badillo will *carry* the election easily. _____

6. (a) The building *lot* was located on a hillside. _____

(b) There was a *lot* of food left for me. _____

(c) An apartment house is going up on the *lot* next door. _____

7. (a) It takes *nerve* to make a parachute jump. _____

(b) The *nerve* in this tooth is dead. _____

(c) Halfway up the cliff, Tom lost his *nerve* and came back down. _____

8. (a) The riveter *catches* the red-hot rivet in a pail. _____

(b) Rich leaped high to *catch* the ball. _____

(c) If you leave now, you can *catch* the last bus. _____

9. (a) The club bought a *block* of tickets for the show. _____

23

(b) We had a *block* of seats all together. ——

(c) There is a drugstore in the next *block*. ——

10. (a) The child has a bad *case* of measles. ——

(b) The *case* of wine had been opened. ——

(c) Someone dropped a *case* of eggs on the floor. ——

Lesson 4.   The Meaning That Fits

Most of the words we use in ordinary affairs have several meanings. Often there is some clear connection between the meanings—a common idea—but sometimes the meanings have nothing in common. And sometimes they are even directly opposite to each other.

How, then, is it possible to communicate? How does anyone know what meaning to give a word in a particular sentence?

The fact is that we don't always get across our meaning. Misunderstandings occur. A meeting is missed, the wrong goods are shipped, or people needlessly get their feelings hurt. A statement may be incomplete. Or it may be ambiguous (am•big'u•ous)—capable of being read in more than one way.

For example, take this statement: "The bank has an interest in this building." What does *interest* mean? It might mean

(1) the bank is part owner of the building
(2) the bank is seriously considering purchase of it
(3) the bank likes the building and doesn't want to see it torn down

More words are needed to clear up the question. An earlier sentence or a following sentence might explain. These other sentences are the *context* of the word *interest*. The context of any word consists of the words surrounding it—within the same sentence, in another sentence, or even within the entire paragraph.

Sometimes the context consists not only of the words but of the whole situation in which a word appears. In a law court, the word *battery* means "beating or pounding." In military affairs, it refers to a group of heavy guns. In baseball, a *battery* consists of the pitcher and catcher.

The context determines which meaning of a word is intended by the writer or speaker. Sometimes, of course, the necessary explanation is missing and the reader or listener is left guessing.

No one knows exactly how the brain operates when a word with several meanings appears. But it must act something like a computer. The brain silently and speedily scans the meanings stored in it for the word in question until it comes to one that fits.

The meaning you select for a word must fit in the context. It must make sense. If none of the meanings stored in your brain makes sense, something is wrong. Either the writer erred, or you need more information.

CHECK IT OUT

A. On the basis of the passage you have just read, which of the following statements are correct? Write *true* or *false*.

1. The context of a word consists only of the words that surround it.

_____

2. The context of a word includes the situation in which it is used.

_____

3. Context always determines which meaning of a word is intended by the writer or speaker.

_____

4. The context always gives enough information for you to decide which meaning to give a word.

_____

5. If none of the meanings you have for a word fits in the context, it is likely that the writer or speaker made a mistake.

_____

SEE FOR YOURSELF

B. Two meanings are given for the italicized word in each sentence. Decide which meaning fits. Place an *x* on the line next to it. The first one is done for you.

1. The store will *feature* sports coats next week.

(a) prominently display   _*x*_

(b) write a special article about   _____

26

2. The pitcher was charged with an *error*.

    (a) a misplay   _____

    (b) a wrong belief   _____

3. We were surprised by the umpire's *flare* of anger.

    (a) a bright light   _____

    (b) sudden outburst   _____

4. Many people like the *flavor* of country living.

    (a) the characteristic quality   _____

    (b) taste and smell   _____

5. The *float* in the carburetor was stuck.

    (a) a platform anchored near the shore   _____

    (b) a device for regulating the flow of liquid _____

6. The water mains will be *flushed* out today.

    (a) cleaned out   _____

    (b) made level with the surface   _____

7. You will have to *change* to the local bus at the next stop.

    (a) transfer   _____

    (b) get small coins   _____

8. The doctor changed the baby's *formula*.

    (a) a rule or method for doing something   _____

    (b) a prescription for preparing food   _____

9. Even flour is now *fortified* with vitamins and minerals.

    (a) protected   _____

    (b) enriched   _____

10. The research program *foundered* from lack of money.

(a) stumbled and fell _____

(b) failed _____

C. Three genuine meanings are given for the italicized word in each sentence. Decide which meaning fits. Place an *x* on the line next to it.

1. The drainpipe was *choked* with leaves.

(a) unable to breathe _____

(b) smothered _____

(c) blocked up _____

2. For a minute or two, I *lapsed* into unconsciousness.

(a) slipped _____

(b) ended _____

(c) passed away _____

3. The committee has wide *latitude* in running the business.

(a) distance north and south of the equator _____

(b) freedom of action _____

(c) area _____

4. They hoped to *cover* 300 miles a day on the trip.

(a) protect _____

(b) travel _____

(c) deal with _____

5. Be sure to read the *legend* under the drawing carefully.

(a) an explanation or title _____

(b) an inscription on a coin ____

(c) a story handed down for generations ____

6. The employer is *liable* for any harm suffered by a worker because of faulty equipment.

(a) responsible under the law ____

(b) likely to be ____

(c) subject to ____

7. The newspapers described the candidate as *liberal* in politics.

(a) generous ____

(b) tolerant ____

(c) favoring reforms and progress ____

8. Every day for a month Maria worked to the *limit* of her energy.

(a) the point beyond which it is impossible to go ____

(b) boundary line ____

(c) the greatest amount allowed ____

9. There is no excuse for Tim's *slovenly* speech.

(a) careless ____

(b) untidy ____

(c) shiftless ____

10. It turned out that Felipe's statement was the *literal* truth.

(a) actual ____

(b) using letters of the alphabet ____

(c) using words with their ordinary meaning ____

D. Six real meanings are given for the italicized word in each sentence. Decide which meaning fits. Place an *x* on the line beside it.

1. This bread has no *body* to it.

   (a) the whole structure and substance of a living thing _____

   (b) a corpse _____

   (c) a group of people _____

   (d) the main part of anything _____

   (e) substance and consistency _____

   (f) any natural object in the skies _____

2. The accused man was released on *bond* not to leave the city.

   (a) anything that binds or restrains _____

   (b) a uniting force (bonds of friendship) _____

   (c) a binding agreement or promise _____

   (d) an interest-bearing certificate issued by government or business _____

   (e) a substance such as glue or solder that holds things together _____

   (f) the joining of two pieces of material by such substance _____

3. Let's get to the *bottom* of their antagonism.

   (a) the lowest part of anything _____

   (b) the basic cause or meaning of something _____

   (c) the part on which something rests _____

   (d) the seat of a chair _____

   (e) the lower part of a two-piece garment _____

   (f) the bed underneath a body of water _____

4. The hunters brought us a *brace* of pheasants.

   (a) a device used as a support _____

(b) a device for maintaining tension   ____

(c) a fastener for keeping things in place   ____

(d) two of a kind   ____

(e) a device for supporting a weak part of the body   ____

(f) a tool for holding a bit   ____

5. We will *break* the trip by a stopover in St. Louis.

    (a) to cause to come apart by force (to break a window)   ____

    (b) to interrupt (a coffee break)   ____

    (c) to tame or make obedient (to break a horse)   ____

    (d) to bring to a sudden end (to break off a connection)   ____

    (e) to make known (to break the news)   ____

    (f) to decipher (to break a code)   ____

6. He takes a *broad* view of young people's fads and fancies.

    (a) a large extent from side to side   ____

    (b) obvious, plain to be seen (a broad hint)   ____

    (c) tolerant, liberal   ____

    (d) not detailed   ____

    (e) not limited   ____

    (f) strongly marked (a broad accent)   ____

7. What *business* is it of his where we are going?

    (a) one's work or occupation   ____

    (b) whatever engages one's time or attention   ____

    (c) whatever rightfully concerns one   ____

    (d) a special task or occupation   ____

    (e) a commercial establishment   ____

    (f) actions, pauses, gestures of an actor in a play   ____

8. Beverly Sills will be a great drawing *card* for this concert.

(a) a flat piece of thick paper ____

(b) an item used in games ____

(c) a program of sports events ____

(d) a special attraction as described in a printed program ____

(e) a witty, comical person ____

(f) a printed form bearing information ____

What Do You Mean?

The following statements are ambiguous. That is, they can be given more than one meaning. They need more context. Can you figure out two possible meanings for each statement?

We want more modern music.
My job was keeping him alive.
Are these answers all right?
The dog looked longer than the cat.
Mary agreed to please the boss.
Shall we call her home?
You will find the exit if you go
    right downstairs.

---

9. Jackson *carried* all the districts in the eastern part of the state.

(a) to hold something while moving it ____

(b) to convey ____

(c) to assume the costs of something ____

(d) to win ____

(e) to secure the approval of   _____

(f) to bear the weight of   _____

10. Many auto accidents are caused by fast driving, but that was not the *case* here.

(a) an example or instance   _____

(b) a person or family being helped by doctors or a social agency   _____

(c) the argument of one side in a lawsuit   _____

(d) a convincing argument   _____

(e) any matter requiring study or investigation   _____

(f) what actually exists or happens   _____

Lesson 5. **Check Your Progress**

DID YOU GET THE IDEA?

I. Read over the first part of each of the four lessons you have just finished. Then check out the following statements. Write *true* or *false* after each one.

1. You can understand the meaning of a paragraph without knowing the exact meaning of all the words. _____

2. Word meanings are not part of your vocabularies. _____

3. A word that you know may be used with a meaning that you are not used to. _____

4. To name something new, it is easier to invent a new word than to use a familiar word. _____

5. A familiar word gets a new meaning when we use it to name something new. _____

6. You can get all of the meanings of a new word the first time you see it if you study it hard enough. _____

7. All the meanings of a word have something in common. _____

8. The context of a word consists of the words used with it plus the situation in which it is used. _____

9. The context usually determines which meaning of a word is intended because only one meaning fits. _____

10. Every English word has more than one meaning. _____

MAKE IT WORK

II. In each pair of sentences, the same word is *italicized*. Decide whether its meaning is the same in both sentences. Write *same* or *different* on the line provided.

1. Everyone should learn a good *trade*.
   The jeweler's *trade* requires a steady hand.   _____

2. Jack was *trying* to clean up the ship.
   A nurse's job is sometimes very *trying*.   _____

3. There was a *touch* of spring in the air.
   Please don't *touch* the exhibits.   _____

4. Maria climbed to the *top* of the tree.
   There is a restaurant at the *top* of the building.   _____

5. The performance *topped* anything he had done before.
   The dessert was *topped* by bits of chocolate.   _____

6. The *board* of health closed the delicatessen.
   The *board* of education meets once every month.   _____

7. I get *tired* of hearing complaints all day long.
   Ella soon grew *tired* of waiting.   _____

8. The fire *threw* hundreds of workers out of their jobs.
   Pedro *threw* a shoe at the cat.   _____

9. I can't follow the *thread* of the argument.
   We lost the *thread* of the conversation.   _____

10. The measurements must be very *exact*.
    This is the *exact* spot where I found the purse.   _____

III. Watch for the turn in meaning. The italicized word has the
     same meaning in two sentences in each group. It has a
     different meaning in the third. Find this sentence and place
     an *x* on the line next to it.

1. (a) I *see* what you mean.   _____

   (b) I don't *see* how it could have happened.   _____

   (c) We did not *see* the person jump.   _____

2. (a) There was an interesting *account* of the balloon race in the paper.   _____

   (b) How do you *account* for the new interest in chess?   _____

   (c) Dorothy Johnson wrote an *account* of the West.   _____

3. (a) Buttermilk does not *agree* with me. _____

(b) The committee could not *agree* on a name. _____

(c) We all *agree* that the street should be closed. _____

4. (a) The mountain *air* is clean and clear. _____

(b) You will have a chance to *air* your complaints. _____

(c) Let's open the windows and get some fresh *air*. _____

5. (a) At one time everyone wrote with quill *pens*. _____

(b) The mink were kept in *pens* on the hillside. _____

(c) The President signed the bill with seven *pens*. _____

6. (a) The clerk handed me two *books* of matches. _____

(b) You can also borrow *books* from the state library. _____

(c) More than 30,000 *books* are published every year. _____

7. (a) Turn left at the *fork* in the road. _____

(b) There was silver *fork* lying in the road. _____

(c) A little further down, you come to a *fork* in the river. _____

8. (a) We all sat around the *table*. _____

(b) There is a *table* of charts and maps in the book. _____

(c) Put the flowers in the center of the *table*. _____

9. (a) The next *step* is to fill in the cracks with putty. _____

(b) She suddenly announced that she was not going another *step*. _____

(c) Take one *step* backward. _____

10. (a) Her speech was interrupted by *waves* of applause. _____

(b) The *waves* have worn round holes in the rock. _____

(c) The force of the *waves* threatened to shatter the little boat. _____

IV. Three meanings are given for the italicized word in each sentence. Choose the one that fits. Write an *x* on the line next to it.

1. They made a *vain* attempt to keep the boat from turning over.
   (a) having high regard for one's self   _____
   (b) unsuccessful   _____
   (c) of no real value   _____

2. Sometimes you have to *dig* for the meaning of a word.
   (a) break and turn up the ground   _____
   (b) poke or jab   _____
   (c) find out by careful study   _____

3. She spoke in a serious *vein* for several minutes.
   (a) manner or mood   _____
   (b) blood vessel   _____
   (c) part of a leaf structure   _____

4. As time *wore* on the town grew smaller.
   (a) to last well   _____
   (b) to pass on gradually   _____
   (c) to have on one's body   _____

5. Let's get another doctor's *view* on what should be done.
   (a) within sight   _____
   (b) an opinion or judgment   _____
   (c) a photograph of a scene   _____

6. They had a brief *vision* of living in luxury.
   (a) power of eyesight   _____

(b) mental picture   ——

(c) a prophecy   ——

7. The country was *visited* by revolution and disorder.

    (a) bringing suffering and trouble   ——

    (b) going to see or stay with someone   ——

    (c) conversing or chatting with   ——

8. The workers believed they should have a *voice* in how the shop was run.

    (a) the ability to speak or sing   ——

    (b) speech sounds   ——

    (c) the right to take part in   ——

9. The foreman gave his *version* of what had happened.

    (a) an individual's account   ——

    (b) translation   ——

    (c) a different form of a work (the movie version)   ——

10. The jury is now *weighing* the evidence.

    (a) seeing how heavy something is   ——

    (b) choosing carefully   ——

    (c) considering   ——

V.   The word *gather* may mean:
    (a) to come together in one place
    (b) to collect things from various places
    (c) to harvest
    (d) to get an idea
    (e) to gain gradually

Decide which meaning applies to *gather* in each sentence.
Write the letter of the meaning on the line provided.

1. I *gather* that you disagree with us.   ____

2. The neighbors *gathered* at the schoolhouse.   ____

3. The ship slowly *gathered* speed.   ____

4. Willis *gathered* his possessions and moved away.   ____

5. They *gather* three crops each year.   ____

6. The visitors *gathered* the impression that we are unfriendly. ____

7. Several hundred people *gathered* at the airport.   ____

8. Mrs. Mellon *gathered* paintings from all over Europe.   ____

9. The students *gathered* all the papers in the neighborhood.   ____

10. Bit by bit, the army *gathered* strength.   ____

Lesson 6. **The Writer's Signals**

The context of a word consists of the other words surrounding it and the situation in which it is used. In the situation of a hospital, the word *operation* means one thing; in business and industry it means something else.

Context always determines which meaning of a word is intended by the writer. Usually, the sentence in which the word appears is enough context to do the job, but sometimes a key word in a sentence may be read in two different ways. Thus, the sentence *We want more modern music* by itself could mean either

We want *more music* that is modern.

or

We want music that is *more modern.*

When you meet a statement of this sort, you look to the sentences before or after it in order to clear up the meaning. Thus you might find "*We are beginning to like this modern music. We want more modern music (more of the same).*" Or you might find "*There is too much old music on the programs. We want more modern music (more modern than what we have been hearing).*" Context, as you see, may consist of other sentences near the word in question.

Context *always* determines meaning; quite often it also reveals meaning.

Writers often take it for granted that the terms they use will be understood. But to avoid confusion or difficulty, careful writers take time to explain their terms. Your textbooks are written in this way. Every public bill presented in Congress has a section defining the terms that appear in it.

In literary works, newspapers, magazines, and other general reading, the writer does not usually pause for explanation. You should not expect to find carefully planted signals of word meaning in everything you read. But when the signals occur, all you need to do is pay attention: the writer has done the work for you.

Writers use three kinds of clues to help the reader. (1) A **definition** gives the exact meaning that the writer intends for a word. (2) An **example** shows the kind of thing to which a term applies. (3) In a **restatement** the writer states the meaning of a term in familiar words.

These clues are usually introduced by signal words that tell you what is coming. You will find, though, that in a definition the signal words are not at the beginning. Dashes and parentheses are also used as signals. Here are some of the words and phrases used by writers to signal clues to meaning.

Context Clues

Definition	Example	Restatement
consists of	for example	in other words
is	for instance	that is
means	such	or
is called	such as	to put it another way
refers to	like	
	especially	

The word *or* does not always signal a restatement. It may also indicate a choice: You can have coffee *or* tea. A restatement signaled by *or* is always set off by commas:

> A simple majority, *or* more than half, is required to pass the bill.

Notice how these signals are used in the sentences below.

Definition

> The voter's *franchise* **is** his right to vote.
> An unreasonable and lasting fear of something **is called** a *phobia*.
> By *gratuitous*, I **mean** something unjust and uncalled for.
> A *consort* (the husband or wife of a king or queen) does not share the ruler's powers.

Example

> *Extractive industries*, **such as** mining and lumbering, use up our natural resources.
> The gardener needs to study the *soil conditions* of his plot, **especially** the amount of humus and the degree of acidity.

Restatement

> Later, Congress voted to *augment*, **or** increase, the job-training program.
> The woman had been sentenced to five years in prison, but the governor *commuted*—reduced—the sentence to two years.
> *X-ray therapy*, **that is**, treatment by use of X-rays, often halts the growth of the tumor.

CHECK IT OUT

A. On the basis of what you have just read, which of the following statements are correct? Write *true* or *false* on the lines provided.

1. Any sentence containing an unusual or technical term provides all the clues you need to figure out the meaning. _____

2. Context always provides clues to the meaning of a word. _____

3. In a restatement clue, the writer gives an example of what he means by a word he has used. _____

4. The words *such as*, *for example*, and *that is*, are likely to signal that a meaning clue is to follow. _____

5. You will find more context clues in carefully written textbooks than in newspapers. _____

Note: In the work that follows, some of the italicized words will be unfamiliar to you. This is exactly the way things are in everyone's reading. Don't be afraid of strange words. You are learning how to get meanings for them.

DO IT YOURSELF

B. What kind of clue is introduced by each of the following words and phrases? Write *definition*, *example*, or *restatement*. The first one is done for you.

1. consists of   _definition_

6. what this means   _____

2. in other words   _____

7. such   _____

3. such as   _____

8. or   _____

4. that is   _____

9. we mean   _____

5. is called   _____

10. for instance   _____

C. Find the signal words that introduce a definition, example, or restatement in each sentence. Write them on the line provided. The first one is done for you.

1. There was a dangerous crack in the gantry; that is, in the framework on which the crane is carried.   _____ *that is* _____

2. The chemical work of digestion is performed by enzymes such as pepsin and rennin.   _____

3. The thin-walled collecting chamber of the heart is called the right auricle.   _____

4. The stem of a tree, in other words its trunk, branches, and twigs, performs several functions.   _____

5. Mexican cooking makes generous use of peppers, mustard, and curry; such condiments add relish to the food.   _____

6. The timpani, or kettledrums, not only reinforce certain tones but also often determine the beat. _____

7. The President is empowered to prorogue the Congress if the two Houses disagree on an adjournment date; that is, he can call the session to an end. _____

8. The museum is now displaying kinetic art; what this means is sculpture or assemblies involving the use of moving parts and of shifting lights and sounds. _____

9. The prime minister then called for a division of the House; to put it another way, he called for a vote on the bill. _____

10. Evidence from fossils, especially the remains of ferns and other plants, indicates that there was once a forest where the South Pole is now located. _____

TRY AGAIN

D. Find the signal words that introduce a clue to the meaning of the italicized term. Write them on the lines provided.

1. The dams on our rivers produce *hydroelectric power*; that is, electricity produced by the power of falling water. _____

2. The term *New Immigration* refers to people who arrived in America from other countries after 1885. _____

3. The ocean's *salinity*, or salt content, varies from place to place. _____

4. The cells of many plants and animals also produce *nonliving matter*, such as the woody fibers in trees and the shells of coral animals. _____

5. The ocean floor has *surface features* similar to those of dry land; for example, plains, trenches, canyons, and mountains. _____

6. The earth's *hydrosphere* consists of the water on its surface, water vapor in the air, and even water that has soaked into the soil. _____

7. *Convenience foods* like precooked French fries, cake mixes, and frozen pies are expensive but save time and are easy to get ready. _____

8. The *eye* of a cyclone, in other words its center, is an area of calm with no wind, rain, or clouds. _____

9. A large part of the milk sold today is *homogenized* (hom•o′gen•ized) milk; what this means is that the milk has been treated so that the fat particles are evenly scattered throughout. _____

10. *Organic material*, such as shells, bones, and plants, may be preserved as fossils. _____

E. The sentences in **D** above explain ten technical terms. Using this information, decide whether the following statements are correct. Write *yes* or *no*. The first one is done for you.

1. An automobile engine is an example of hydroelectric power. _*no*_

2. Europeans who came to this country after World War I are part of the New Immigration. _____

3. Salinity refers to the amount of impurity in water. _____

4. The shell of a clam is nonliving matter. _____

5. Sunlight is an example of a surface feature of dry land. _____

6. The sea is part of the earth's hydrosphere. _____

7. It doesn't take very long to get convenience foods ready. _____

8. The outer edge of a cyclone is its eye. _____

9. Fat particles have been removed from homogenized milk. _____

10. A dandelion is an example of organic material. _____

F. In each sentence a clue is provided to the meaning of the italicized word or phrase. Following the sentence, there are two statements. Decide whether they are correct. Write *true* or *false*. The first one is done for you.

1. An *echoic* word is one that is formed in imitation of a sound, "tinkle," for example.

    (a) Both of the words *boom* and *crash* are echoic.   *true*

    (b) Both of the words *study* and *arithmetic* are echoic.   *false*

2. Members of Congress receive thousands of letters from their *constituents* (con•stit′u•ents), that is, the voters in their districts.

    (a) The constituents of members of Congress are the people who voted for them. _____

    (b) The constituents of members of Congress are all the citizens over 18 years of age living in the district represented. _____

3. *Extrasensory perception* consists of the ability to perceive things without use of the usual five senses.

    (a) Accurately describing a person one has never seen is an act of extrasensory perception. _____

    (b) Forecasting the weather is an act of extrasensory perception. _____

4. Newspaper headlines often show the *bias*, or feeling, of the writer about the news story.

    (a) A headline that shows bias simply states the facts. _____

(b) If a headline is biased, it is slanted in favor of or against the report in the news story.   _____

5. Some flowers do best in *partial sunlight*; in other words, in a few hours of direct sunlight every day.

(a) Partial sunlight refers to sunlight for part of a day.   _____

(b) If a plant receives direct sunlight all day long, it is not getting partial sunlight.   _____

Lesson 7.   **Connectors**

Let's look again at some of the important ideas about words and meanings presented in earlier lessons.

Most words in common use have several meanings.

Context determines which meaning of a word is intended in a particular sentence.

Your understanding of a word grows gradually as you have more experience with it.

You never get all of the meanings of a word from any one meeting with it.

Writers often provide signal words and clues to the meaning they want the reader to give a word.

When you use context clues, then, to deal with an unfamiliar word, you get only *part* of its meaning. Unless a term is *defined*, context clues do not usually give you an exact meaning. They simply give you enough meaning to make sense of the passage you are reading. This much, of course, is a very great help.

Writers have another way of helping the reader. They use a class of words that we will call **connectors** to show how one word is related to another and how one statement is related to another.

Three kinds of relation are especially important in reading: *contrast, time,* and *cause—effect.*

Contrast.   Let's be sure what *contrast* means. If two things are in contrast, they are sharply different from each other. Red and green are contrasting colors. A long paragraph is in contrast to a short one; that is, it differs in length.

One statement is in contrast to another if it states a different idea. The contrast is signaled by connecting words which join the two differing ideas together. The following words are used as connectors to signal contrast:

although	nevertheless	still
but	nonetheless	while

| by contrast | on the contrary | yet |
| however | on the other hand | |

Usually, these connectors appear between statements, but *although* and *while* may sometimes come at the start of the sentence.

1. It is an interesting book, *although* it is very long. (*interest* and *length* are in contrast)
2. *Although* it is very long, it is an interesting book.
3. *While* we liked the house, it was too big for us. (*liking* and *bigness* are in contrast)
4. It was raining hard; *nevertheless*, we started out.
5. Jack was popular with the men; *on the other hand*, Bill was a better leader.
6. We all liked the idea of putting in sewers; *still*, the cost was more than we could stand.
7. Caputo was new in Congress; *yet*, he got a lot done.

The key word in contrasts is the word *but*. Try using it in place of the other connectors in the sentences above. You will see that it fits all of them except *while* in sentence 3. But see how this sentence can be turned around:

The house was too big for us, *but* we liked it.

Time. There are three ways of looking at time which we will refer to as *earlier*, *during*, and *later*. This is not the same as past, present, and future. Of two things that happened in the past, one may have occurred *earlier* than the other, or they may have been going on during the same time. The following connectors are used to signal time relations:

Earlier	*During*	*Later*
at the outset	while	after
before	meanwhile	finally
beginning with	when	second, third, etc.
first	whenever	then
until		in the end

49

Note that *while* may signal either time or contrast.

> *Time*: Do not open the windows *while* the air conditioners are on.
> *Contrast*: *While* the house was attractive, it was too small for us.

Cause—Effect. One thing is a cause. Another thing is the effect of that cause. You could also say this another way: one thing is the *reason* and another thing is the *result*. This kind of relation between statements is signaled by the following connectors:

Cause (Reason)	*Effect* (Result)	
because	accordingly	so that
for	as a consequence	therefore
for this reason	as a result	thus
since	consequently	

In some sentences the cause is given first. In others the effect comes first. The connectors help you keep cause and effect straight.

> *Because* there were not enough passengers (cause), the flight was canceled (effect).
> The flight was canceled (effect) *since* there were not enough passengers (cause).
> The engine caught on fire (cause) *so that* the train was delayed for two hours (effect).
> Tom found the test hard (effect), *for* he had missed several classes (cause).
> A policeman waved us on (cause); *accordingly*, we drove right through the water (effect).
> We have a season ticket (cause); *thus*, we can get in to all of the games (effect).

Notice that *since* may signal *cause* as well as *time*.

> *Cause*: People use the stairs *since* the elevators are slow.
> *Time*: We have made many friends *since* we moved here.

MAKE IT WORK

A. Decide which meaning each connector signals. Write *time*, *contrast*, or *effect* on the line provided. The first one is done for you.

1. on the other hand   ___*contrast*___
6. finally   _____

2. nonetheless   _____
7. still   _____

3. accordingly   _____
8. so that   _____

4. whenever   _____
9. on the contrary   _____

5. although   _____
10. yet   _____

B. Find the connector in each sentence. Underline it. Decide what relation it signals. Write *earlier*, *during*, *later*, *cause*, or *effect*. The first one is done for you.

1. Ashe seemed very relaxed <u>before</u> the game started.   ___*earlier*___

2. The governor knew she could trust Martinez; accordingly, he was given important tasks to perform.   _____

3. You should beat the eggs until they turn light yellow in color.   _____

4. The manager was upset, for no one had told her about the delays.   _____

5. The driver was in the hospital for six weeks; meanwhile, he had no income.   _____

6. Since the directions were not clear, we will excuse your mistake.   _____

7. We waited for three hours; finally, the doors were opened.   _____

8. You must be sure to roll up the awnings before you leave.   _____

9. She had decided to resign; then something happened to change her mind. _____

10. The pipes have never been replaced; as a result, the water is discolored. _____

11. The book was sent by first-class mail so that it arrived the next day. _____

12. The telephone rang while I was taking a bath. _____

13. You should try to come to see us whenever you are in the neighborhood. _____

14. It rained all through the game; consequently, there were many fumbles. _____

15. It was five o'clock and I was just going out the door when the boss called me. _____

16. The headlight shutters go up after you turn on the lights. _____

17. The weather has been very pleasant since the wind died down. _____

18. While the ants stored their food away, the grasshopper played all day. _____

19. He was eager for the day to begin and was ready to get up before the alarm went off. _____

20. There has been little rain; as a consequence, the streams have dried up. _____

C. Find the connector in each sentence. Decide whether it signals contrast, cause, or effect. Write *contrast*, *cause*, or *effect* on the line provided. The first two are done for you.

1. The movie was quite good, although it did not follow the book. _____*contrast*_____

2. The movie was quite good since it did not follow the book. _____*cause*_____

3. She was a busy person; yet, she was always willing to talk with us. _____

4. The car is too expensive; on the other hand, it will last a long time. _____

5. The main road was torn up so that we had to take a detour. _____

6. Since there were no more questions, the meeting was adjourned. _____

7. The building is known to be a firetrap; therefore, it must be closed. _____

8. The food was very plain and simply prepared; still, there was plenty of it. _____

9. While he is very young, he has had a great deal of experience. _____

10. The senator is not in bad health; on the contrary, she is very fit. _____

D. Three possible meanings are given for the italicized part of each numbered sentence. Decide which meaning is correct and place an *x* on the line next to it.

1. She decided not to retype the letter *since there were only two mistakes.*

   (a) after making only two mistakes _____

   (b) because there were two mistakes _____

   (c) because there were only two mistakes _____

2. The water has tasted odd *ever since they started to add fluoride.*

   (a) because they added fluoride _____

   (b) although they added fluoride _____

   (c) after they added fluoride _____

3. The newspaper will not be delivered *while we are away*.

    (a) during the time we are away   _____

    (b) although we are away   _____

    (c) because we are away   _____

4. *While the book was interesting*, it was hard to read.

    (a) Because the book was interesting   _____

    (b) During the time that the book was interesting   _____

    (c) Although the book was interesting   _____

5. We tried to make her comfortable *until the ambulance arrived*.

    (a) after the ambulance arrived   _____

    (b) before the ambulance arrived   _____

    (c) when the ambulance arrived   _____

6. We offered to deliver her package *since we were driving past her house*.

    (a) as we were driving past her house   _____

    (b) after we drove past her house   _____

    (c) because we were driving past her house   _____

    For the items below, decide which of the three sentences best expresses the meaning of the numbered sentence. Place an *x* on the line next to it.

7. We hurried to set the table; meanwhile, the beans boiled dry.

    (a) The beans boiled dry because we set the table.   _____

    (b) The beans boiled dry while we were setting the table. _____

    (c) The beans boiled dry although we set the table.   _____

8. Our candidate was not well known; nevertheless, she won the election.

    (a) She won because she was not well known.   _____

(b) She won after she was well known.   _____

(c) She won although she was not well known.   _____

9. Keep your seat belt fastened until the light goes off.

   (a) Keep it fastened after the light goes off.   _____

   (b) Keep it fastened before the light goes off.   _____

   (c) Keep it fastened even though the light goes off.   _____

10. The power was off for two days; as a result, the food in our freezer spoiled.

   (a) The power was off even though the food was spoiled.   _____

   (b) The food was spoiled before the power went off.   _____

   (c) The food was spoiled because the power went off.   _____

Lesson 8.   Clues from Sentence Structure

It is only fair to say that in a great deal of your reading you will not find definitions, examples, and restatements to help with an unfamiliar word. Nor will you always find connectors to keep the meaning straight.

Without these helps, digging out the meaning is harder work, but it is not impossible. In this lesson and in the one that follows we will suggest some ways of going at it.

One source of help lies in sentence structure. The word *structure* usually refers to the way something is put together. The structure of a building is the way its parts are put together: the foundation, upright supports, crossbeams, roof, etc.

The structure of a sentence is the arrangement of its parts: subject, verb, complements, and modifiers. In the sentence

Man bites dog.

you know who did the biting and who got bitten just from the arrangement, the order in which the words appear.

Knowing how English sentences are constructed is a great help in reading, but at this point we are concerned only with modifiers. A modifier is a word or group of words that goes with another word and tells something about it. The job of a modifier is to identify or describe the word it goes with. And usually it goes right before or right after that word.

The man *who was attacked* bit the dog.
The man bit the dog *that attacked him.*

Any word group that provides information about an unfamiliar word is a clue to its meaning. See how this works in the following sentences in which the modifiers are italicized:

The kings and nobles relied upon the **seneschals**, *the supervisors of their households*, to manage everyday details of living.

56

The **maitre d'hotel**, *who plans the menus, supervises the food shopping, and directs the waiters*, is the key man in a restaurant.

The **M-1 money supply**, *which is the money in people's pockets and checking accounts*, has been growing steadily.

The **documentary film**, *portraying the actual details of an event or social condition*, has always been popular.

TRY IT OUT

A. There is a modifying word group attached to the italicized word in each sentence. Find the word group and underline it.

1. The *bailiff*, a deputy sheriff, led the jury out to lunch.

2. The table is covered with a green *baize*, a thick, woolen cloth somewhat like felt.

3. Feeding on tuna and other large fish, the *dolphin* is called "killer whale" by fishermen.

4. To keep canned foods from spoiling, *preservatives* are added.

5. The man was imprisoned for *arson*, having set fire to three buildings in the town.

B. One of the statements that follow each numbered sentence is correct. The others are not. Use the clues to the meaning of the italicized word to find the correct statement. Place an *x* on the line next to it.

1. Many businessmen act on *intuition*, which is immediate understanding of a situation without consciously thinking about it.

(a) Intuition requires time for careful study. _____

(b) Intuition is a quick response to a situation. _____

(c) If a person acts on intuition, he has thought a good deal about what he is going to do. _____

2. *Introspection*, looking into one's mind and feelings, is sometimes helpful, but it is not a scientific way of proceeding.

   (a) Introspection is based upon experiments that others can repeat. _____

   (b) Introspection provides information about why other people act as they do. _____

   (c) Introspection provides information only about one's self. _____

3. Congress has worked for years to revise the U.S. criminal *code*, the orderly publication of laws concerning federal crimes.

   (a) A code is a systematic arrangement of laws. _____

   (b) A code explains the meaning of the laws. _____

   (c) A code is written in secret symbols known only to lawyers. _____

4. The engineers set up a *cofferdam*, which is a temporary watertight structure, to change the course of the river while they built the foundation of the bridge.

   (a) A cofferdam is a protection for a bridge. _____

   (b) A cofferdam keeps water out of a working area. _____

   (c) A cofferdam is a dam that protects lowlands from flooding by a river. _____

5. There were several *discrepancies* in the story, statements that contradicted each other.

   (a) A discrepancy is a lie. _____

   (b) A discrepancy is a statement made to confuse a reader or listener. _____

   (c) If there is a discrepancy in a story, the story contains two statements that disagree. _____

6. The *horizon*, where the earth seems to meet the sky, seems far away in the clear mountain air.

   (a) You can see the horizon only straight ahead of you. _____

   (b) You can't see the horizon on a dark night. _____

   (c) Anything on the horizon looks very large. _____

7. Green and blue are restful *hues* that tend to fade in the sunlight.

    (a) A hue is a color.   _____

    (b) Purple and gray are not hues.   _____

    (c) Sunshine is a hue.   _____

8. Before receiving a license to practice, a doctor must spend at least a year as an *intern* working in a hospital under supervision of experienced physicians and surgeons.

    (a) An intern is not a doctor.   _____

    (b) An intern can set up his own office and practice medicine in a community.   _____

    (c) An intern is a doctor who serves as a student or apprentice in a hospital.   _____

9. The *economy* of a nation, which is its system of producing, distributing, and consuming wealth, depends upon the energy and good sense of its people.

    (a) A presidential election is part of our economy.   _____

    (b) A snowstorm is part of our economy.   _____

    (c) Farming is part of our economy.   _____

10. In this season, the *prevailing* winds, those usually blowing from the same direction, come from the west.

    (a) When you speak of the direction from which winds usually blow, you speak of prevailing winds.   _____

    (b) The strongest winds in an area are its prevailing winds.   _____

    (c) A prevailing wind is one that destroys everything in its path.   _____

TRY AGAIN

C. Two statements following each sentence are false. One is true. Find the correct statement and place an *x* on the line next to it.

1. Two witnesses came forward to *corroborate* the driver's account, bearing out what he told the jury.

   (a) To corroborate something is to deny it. ____

   (b) To corroborate is to work together to get something done. ____

   (c) To corroborate is to support or verify. ____

2. The coach was *adamant*, not yielding an inch from his decision to suspend the players.

   (a) If you are adamant, you are unwilling to change. ____

   (b) To be adamant is to be uncertain. ____

   (c) To be adamant is to be unable to make a decision. ____

3. Dr. Barnard was a member of an agricultural *mission* to India, a group of experts on better farming methods.

   (a) A mission is a group of immigrants. ____

   (b) A mission is a group of tourists. ____

   (c) A mission is a group sent abroad to provide help to a foreign country. ____

4. The *theme* of a story, which is its central meaning, expresses the author's point of view about life.

   (a) The theme is what happens to the characters. ____

   (b) The theme is the underlying meaning of what happens in a story. ____

   (c) The theme of a story is the way it turns out. ____

5. Weather experts say that a drought is *imminent*, likely to occur at any time this year or next.

   (a) An imminent danger is one close at hand. ____

   (b) If a drought is imminent, it will not occur for many years. ____

   (c) An imminent drought is not very serious. ____

Lesson 9.   Words Work Together

You have met three kinds of clues to word meaning: *signal words* for definitions, examples, and restatements; *connectors* that tie one word or idea to another; and *word groups* that modify, identify, and explain.

All of these clues are right out in the open and are easy to spot. They point not only to the meaning of a word but to the meaning of the whole passage in which they occur.

Still, you will be reading a good many paragraphs as you go along in which there are no outright, planted, visible clues. There is nothing for you to do but to dig out the meaning on your own.

Fortunately, there are other clues which you can learn to spot when you know what to look for. They arise from the fact that words work together to express the writer's meaning. Words have to work together, or no one could make himself understood.

First, most sentences consist of groups of words that are put together in predictable ways. You have learned to read the whole of a group rather than one word at a time; for example:

The men   in the boat   did not know   the color   of the sky.

Second, you have learned something else about reading that you may not realize. Usually, you cannot be sure what meaning to place on words at the start of a sentence until you come to the end. For example:

The *object*...

Object might mean: (1) a thing that can be seen or touched; (2) a part of a sentence; or (3) a goal or purpose. The rest of the sentence will help you decide the meaning.

Let's go on with the sentence, step by step.

The object of the game is to...
The object of the game is to score...
The object of the game is to score the least number...
The object of the game is to score the least number of points.

By the time you get through reading *of the game*, you know the meaning of *object*. But you don't know the meaning of the whole sentence until the last word is reached. Because the meaning is unusual, you may want to go back and reread the whole sentence.

A paragraph may operate in the same way. The writer may use the entire paragraph to provide clues to the meaning of one word. For example, notice how the meaning of *jeopardy* is made clear in the following paragraph.

> Early last week a state inspector discovered a serious new crack in the old stone dam near Kent. Without realizing it, the people living in the valley below the dam had been living in **jeopardy** for weeks, possibly for months. There was a *danger* that the dam would give way, and if it did, they could not escape the *peril* to their lives. The millions of gallons of water *threatened destruction* of farms, homes and other property that might lie in its path. Immediate steps were taken to lower the water level, and some people were moved out of the valley to safer quarters.

This paragraph gives you two kinds of help. First, it contains words that have the same meaning as *jeopardy*. The words *danger*, *peril*, and *threatened destruction* can all be used in place of *jeopardy*. Second, the two sentences following "living in jeopardy" give examples of what the phrase means.

Sometimes a writer will explain a word by saying what it does *not* mean; for example,

> The man was a *notorious* bungler, and by *notorious* I do not mean "noted" or "famous." His record of failure was well known, but it was widey disapproved.

Thus, examples, substitute words, and negative statements are genuine clues to meaning. They help the reader not only with a particular word, but with the meaning of a whole sentence or paragraph.

TRY THESE

A. One word or phrase in each paragraph is set in **boldface**. Clues to its meaning are in *italics*. An unfinished definition

appears below each paragraph. Figure out which clue word
will complete the meaning, and write it on the line provided.

1. Fourteen years after it was opened, the beautiful home of the New York Philharmonic was torn apart. Seats and floor coverings were taken up. The balconies were removed. The hall was stripped back to bare walls. All this was done because the **acoustics** of the hall were not right. The bass *tones* had always been dead. Orchestra members complained that they could not *hear* each other playing. Nowhere in the hall were the *sounds* of the orchestra bright and satisfying.

acoustics means "the way in which ____ are heard." _____

2. At exactly one o'clock in the afternoon of March 26, the lights dimmed in Madison Square Garden. The ringmaster stepped into the spotlight and announced, "Ladies and gentlemen, the greatest show on earth," and the circus began. For 20 hours before, a staff of nearly 500 had followed a *detailed schedule* in moving lions, tigers, elephants, and equipment through the city streets to their *assigned places* in the stadium. *Step by step*, the workers transformed the inside of the Garden into a circus setting. Every part of the job was done in *regular order*. By noon, every piece of equipment and every performer was in place. The miracle had been performed by **precision timing**.

precision timing means "doing things exactly on ____ ." _____

3. Automation became possible with the development of computers that were "intelligent" enough to correct their own mistakes. A *whole manufacturing system* can now be set up in which a machine—the *computer*—can be used to *control other machines*. Raw material entering the factory is *guided* by an electronic brain through a whole series of manufacturing processes. The computer is used to *give instructions* to the machines, to examine their work, to make any needed corrections, and to control the packaging of the finished product.

automation means "control of a manufacturing process by
means of a ____ ." _____

4. In late 1814, Americans under the command of General Andrew Jackson won the Battle of New Orleans. The British force was one of the largest that had ever been assembled. Against them, Jackson led a **motley** group. There were troops from the regular army, New Orleans militia, sailors, and a battalion of San Domingo troops. They spoke *different* languages. They wore a *variety* of uniforms or no uniforms at all. There were a battalion of free Negroes, companies of frontiersmen from

Tennessee and Kentucky, and the swarthy crews from two of the pirate ships of Jean Lafitte. This *mixed* force soundly defeated the veteran British army and compelled them to withdraw.

motley means "composed of many ____ elements."   _____

5. The most amazing thing about education in the United States is the number of **avenues of reentry** it offers. The *doors are never closed*. People of any age and in any location may *pick up again* where they left off. A large part of those who receive college degrees had interrupted their studies for a time and *returned* to take them up *once more*. Many *ways* are *open* for continuing education outside the regular school system. Members of the armed forces may enroll in correspondence courses to complete high school or college work. Every department in the federal government provides *opportunities* for employees to take courses. There are 35,000 private schools which offer courses for adults in trades and other interests. These *pathways for beginning again* are open to everyone, and millions of Americans follow them every year.

avenues of reentry means " ____ to begin again."   _____

B. There are several clues for the italicized word in each paragraph. Find those words or phrases and write them on the lines provided. For each paragraph, one clue is provided.

1. The Forty-Niners engaged in gold mining led a *precarious* life. The gain from their work was always uncertain. Their work was hazardous. They lived in unhealthy conditions. They were unsure that a day of hard work would yield any gold dust.

Clues: (a) _____*uncertain*_____   (c) _____

         (b) _____   (d) _____

2. We usually think of *enterprise* in connection with business, but it can appear in any other part of our national life as well. The bold program for landing astronauts on the moon is an example. The courageous exploration of the ocean floor is another. The daring venture of crossing the North Pole in a submarine is an example of enterprise. The scientist, too, who undertakes an important research is engaging in enterprise.

Clues: (a) _____*bold program*_____   (c) _____

         (b) _____   (d) _____

3. If you are filling out an income tax return, you report all of the income you have received. But you do not have to pay a tax on all this income. You are allowed certain *exemptions*, sums which are not taxed. You are allowed a personal exemption of $1,000, which you subtract from the total income you report. You are also allowed to deduct the same amount if you are blind or over 65. And you may also take out $1,000 for your spouse and for each of your children under 19 in certain cases. These exemptions are subtracted from the total reported income in figuring out the amount on which you pay a tax.

Clues: (a) ____*sums not taxed*____   (c) _____

  (b) _____   (d) _____

4. It is not a crime to tell a lie to your friends. But if you take an oath in court to tell the truth there, it is then a *crime* to lie because the law forbids it. People usually think of crime in terms of robbery, rape, and murder, but you commit a crime any time you break the law. Some laws tell you what you must do; others tell you what you may not do. If you fail to file an income tax return, you have committed a crime because you have failed to do what the law requires. An attempt to burn down your own house would be a crime because it is against the law. Crimes range in seriousness from malicious mischief, such as shooting out street lights, to murder and treason, but they are all crimes because they are in violation of the law.

Clues: (a) ____*law forbids it*____   (d) _____

  (b) _____   (e) _____

  (c) _____

Lesson 10. Check Your Progress

You have learned a great deal about getting the meaning from what you read. You have learned about clues for the meaning of individual words and you have learned something about getting the meaning when no signal words or connectors are present. What you have learned clearly applies not just to single words but to whole paragraphs and passages. Now it is time for a checkup.

You will find it profitable to reread the introductory parts of the last four lessons before going on.

I. Decide what kind of explanation is signaled by each of the following words or phrases. Write *definition*, *example*, or *restatement*.

1. especially _____   6. consists of _____

2. is called _____   7. in other words _____

3. that is _____   8. refers to _____

4. for instance _____   9. for example _____

5. such as _____   10. or _____

II. Decide what relation each of the following words or phrases expresses. Write *time*, *contrast*, *cause*, or *effect*.

1. although _____   6. still _____

2. meanwhile _____   7. until _____

3. consequently _____   8. on the other hand _____

4. because _____   9. so that _____

5. therefore _____   10. finally _____

III. Find the words or phrases that signal a clue to the meaning of the italicized words or phrases. Write them on the lines provided.

1. The big cities need new sources of *revenue*, or income. _____

2. Some method must be provided in any constitution for *amending*, that is, for changing it. _____

3. A pattern of stars visible to the naked eye in a small area of sky is called a *constellation*. _____

4. It may be that the *heavier elements*, such as carbon, oxygen, iron, and sodium, are formed by fusion of lighter elements. _____

5. The social security program provides for temporary *unemployment insurance*; in other words, if a person is out of work he or she is assured of receiving money from the government for a period of months. _____

6. Some of the *extraction industries*, like lumbering and fishing, are replacing the resources they have extracted. _____

7. The school provides training in *culinary arts*, especially in the preparing of sauces and desserts. _____

8. The book deals entirely with the *physical sciences*; for example, geology, oceanography, and chemistry. _____

9. *Spices* such as pepper, mustard, and cloves were once used to hide unpleasant tastes and odors in food as well as to preserve it. _____

10. The city council is required by law to present a *balanced budget*; what this means is that the expected income from taxes, fees, and other sources must equal the expenditures that are proposed. _____

IV. Look for clues to the meaning of the italicized word. Three statements follow each sentence. Only one is correct. Find this statement and place an *x* on the line next to it.

1. The other candidate was a *demagogue*, stirring people up by appeals to their emotions and prejudices.

   (a) A demagogue would rely on sensational charges, catchwords, and smears to win over the voters. _____

   (b) A demagogue would stick to the facts. _____

   (c) Anyone who campaigns hard and speaks forcefully is a demagogue. _____

2. *Ecology*, which deals with relations of living things to their environment, has become important in deciding the location of new industrial plants.

   (a) The increased cost of living is a matter of ecology. _____

   (b) Ecology is concerned with taxes. _____

   (c) Ecology deals with the effect of chemical wastes dumped into rivers and lakes. _____

3. A person charged with a crime may be released on *bail*, a sum of money deposited with the court as a guarantee that the suspect will return for trial at a fixed date.

   (a) Bail is a punishment for committing a crime. _____

   (b) Bail is payment of a fine. _____

   (c) A person giving bail must still stand trial. _____

4. The *mortgagee*, the person who lends money in return for a mortgage, can take over the property if interest payments are not made.

   (a) The mortgagee owns the property on which a mortgage is placed. _____

   (b) The mortgagee pays interest on the money loaned. _____

   (c) The mortgagee receives interest on the money loaned. _____

5. The children were to inherit the property when they reached their *majority*, the age at which they would have full legal rights and responsibilities.

(a) When you reach your majority, you can vote and sign contracts. _____

(b) You reach your majority when you have lived more than half your life. _____

(c) Your majority occurs when more than half the people you know will trust you with responsibilities. _____

V. In each paragraph, one word is italicized. The entire paragraph is an explanation of that word. Several statements appear below the paragraph. Decide which of them are correct. Write *true* or *false* on the lines provided.

1. A *contract* is an agreement between two or more people in which one person agrees to do something by a specified date in return for something done by the other. Usually the contract is a written document signed and dated by both parties. It must state clearly the consideration, that is, what is to be given or done by one person in exchange for what is given or done by the other. If one person does what was promised and the other does not, that other may be sued in court and required by court order to make good. He or she may also be required to pay for damages suffered as a result of the failure to perform. The things to be done by both parties must be stated in definite terms or the court will hold that the contract is too vague and general to be enforced. Similarly, the time period within which the work is to be done must be definite or the court will say that the document is not a contract.

(a) If Mrs. A writes a letter to Mrs. B promising to lend her a sum of money, the letter is a contract. _____

(b) If a person agrees to make a gift before he or she dies to another person, this is not a contract. _____

(c) A contract must be signed by everyone who undertakes in it to do something. _____

(d) If there is no time limit for performance, it can never be held that the agreement has been broken. _____

2. The *atmosphere* of the earth extends about 22 miles above the earth's surface. Above that level the molecules of the gases which make up the air are so far apart that there is no real air at all. If you stuck your head out of a spaceship to catch a breath, you would catch nothing, but your head if uncovered would freeze because of the low temperature. The atmosphere is made up of several layers, each of which does something to us or for us. The layer nearest the earth is our weather-maker. In the next layer, the stratosphere, the movement of the air is horizontal, without sudden updrafts and downdrafts, so jet planes travel comfortably in it. At the top of the third layer, there is the ionosphere, which bounces back to earth the radio waves by which we communicate. If they did not bounce back, the radio waves would go straight out into space.

(a) The atmosphere of the earth is what we call air.   _____

(b) The air in the stratosphere is in such violent motion that it is unsuited to air travel.   _____

(c) The air we breathe is made up of gases.   _____

(d) The stratosphere lies outside the earth's atmosphere.   _____

(e) Radio waves are bounced back to the earth from the stratosphere.   _____

3. "In every language there are two great classes of words which, taken together, comprise the whole vocabulary. First, there are those words with which we become acquainted in ordinary conversation—which we learn from members of our own family and from our familiar associates, and which we should know and be able to use even if we could not read or write. They concern the common things of life. On the other hand, our language includes a multitude of words which are comparatively seldom used in ordinary conversation. Their meanings are known to every educated person but there is little occasion to employ them. Our first acquaintance with them comes from books that we read, lectures that we hear, or the more formal conversation of highly educated speakers, who are discussing some topic in a style appropriately elevated above the habitual level of everyday life. Such words are called *learned* (learn•ed)."

(a) There are not many learned words in our language.   _____

(b) Learned words are seldom used in conversation.   _____

(c) Learned words concern the common things of life.   _____

70

(d) The meanings of learned words are known to only a few
highly educated speakers. _____

(e) We first meet learned words in books or lectures. _____

4. In everyday affairs, the word *intelligence* seems to have a clear-cut meaning. We do not hesitate to say that someone lacks the intelligence (wit, smartness) to do a job. In military affairs, intelligence refers to information, but in the fields of psychology and testing there is some difference of opinion as to what intelligence is. There is agreement that it is not a single faculty but a cluster of related abilities. There is some disagreement as to what these specific abilities are. But in terms of practical results, intelligence can be observed in and identified with (a) the ability to profit from past experience, (b) the ability to learn, and (c) the ability to think either with words or with other symbols.

(a) In the fields of psychology and testing, intelligence refers
to information. _____

(b) Psychologists regard intelligence as a general ability. _____

(c) In psychology, intelligence is thought to be a group of
related abilities. _____

(d) Testers would say that the ability to learn from past
experience is a mark of intelligence. _____

(e) Psychologists believe that the ability to learn has nothing
to do with intelligence. _____

5. When two nations agree to a *détente*, neither one surrenders its claims against the other, nor do they agree to support each other if war occurs. The nations simply agree to relax and get along with each other. They proceed to make treaties and to arrange for an exchange of goods and services. Each nation invites scientists, symphony orchestras, and ballet groups from the other nation to visit. There is cooperation and joint efforts on scientific projects and explorations.

(a) In a détente, the two nations become military allies. _____

(b) A détente is a relaxation of tensions. _____

(c) In a détente, one nation gives up something to the other. _____

(d) A détente permits exchange of knowledge and skills. _____

Lesson 11.   Prefixes

One-syllable words stand alone; that is, they have only one part. Many of these words have been used as a base for building longer words. From base words such as *place*, *see*, and *form*, for example, other words were built by adding parts at the beginning or at the end.

place	*re*place	place*ment*
use	*re*use	use*ful*
form	*re*form	form*ation*

A word part added at the beginning of a word is called a **prefix**. A word part added at the end of a word is called a **suffix**.

English base words may have more than one syllable. For example, from *direct* come the words *indirect* and *direction*. From *cover* come the words *recover* and *covering*. Also, word parts may be added to words that already have prefixes and suffixes.

information   *mis*information   informational

Prefixes and suffixes are added to word **stems** as well as to base words. A stem does not exist as a word by itself. It is simply a word part to which prefixes and suffixes are joined. Thus *fer* and *dict* are word stems that appear in many words: re*fer*, con*fer*, pre*dict*, contra*dict*, etc.

Most of our word stems come from Latin, the language of the ancient Romans. The Romans themselves were great word builders. They made words by adding a prefix to an existing word. Thus, to the verb *pellere* they added prefixes to make *dispellere*, *expellere*, *repellere*.

One meaning of *pellere* was "drive, push, hurl." You can see this meaning and the meaning of the prefix in English words: *dispel* (drive away), *expel* (drive out), and *repel* (drive back).

In some words, however, the meaning of the prefix was lost on the way from Latin to English. As a result, the prefix has no meaning for us in words such as *examine*, *reveal*, *invent*.

72

By contrast, in words built by English people on their own base words, the prefix gives a definite meaning that you can count on: *recount* (count again), *foretell* (tell beforehand). As you see, the meaning of the base word carries over into the words made from it.

English words have also been built with combining forms such as *micro*, *phono*, and *scope*. Most of these forms have only one meaning. They are called combining forms because they can be combined with each other as well as with other word parts: *microscope*, *microphone*, etc.

Here is a list of combining forms and prefixes that have only one meaning.

Combining Forms

Form	*Meaning*	*Example*
bio	life	**bio**graphy
geo	earth	**geo**logy
micro	small	**micro**phone
meter	device for measuring	thermo**meter**
ology	science or study	bi**ology**
phono	sound	**phono**graph
photo	light	**photo**graph
pseudo	false	**pseudo**nym
scope	device for seeing, observing	micro**scope**
tele	distant	**tele**gram

Prefixes With One Meaning

Prefix	*Meaning*	*Example*
auto	self	**auto**mobile
extra	outside	**extra**ordinary
fore	before	**fore**head

73

hyper	too much	*hyper*active
inter	between, among	*inter*state
intra	within	*intra*venous
mal	bad	*mal*treat
mini	small	*mini*skirt
mis	wrong	*mis*take
multi	many	*multi*colored
non	not	*non*resident
post	after, later	*post*date
pre	before, earlier	*pre*fix
ultra	beyond, extremely	*ultra*modern

As you see, adding a prefix or a combining form makes a longer word. But if you know what the added part means, the long word is easy to understand.

DO IT YOURSELF

A. Prefixes are listed on the left. From the list on the right, choose the correct meaning of each prefix. Write it on the line provided. The first one is done for you.

Prefix		*Meaning*
1. extra	_outside_	wrong
2. inter	_____	within
3. auto	_____	small
4. hyper	_____	outside
5. intra	_____	bad
6. multi	_____	between, among
7. mis	_____	many

74

8. fore   _____   too much

9. mal   _____   self

10. mini   _____   before

B. Combining forms are given on the left. From the list on the right, choose the correct meaning of each combining form. Write it on the line provided.

Combining Form		*Meaning*
1. geo	_____	device for measuring
2. meter	_____	study or science
3. ology	_____	device for seeing or observing
4. tele	_____	small
5. bio	_____	light
6. photo	_____	sound
7. pseudo	_____	distant
8. micro	_____	earth
9. phono	_____	life
10. scope	_____	false

C. Each italicized word contains one or two combining forms. The meaning of the sentence depends upon the meaning of the italicized word. Complete each sentence with a word that fits. Write that word in the blank space. The first one is done for you.

75

1. You can see something very _____ *small* _____ with a *microscope*.

2. A doctor uses a *stethoscope* to _____ the condition of your heart and lungs. (*steth* means "chest")

3. *Biology* is the study of _____.

4. A *photometer* is a device for measuring _____.

5. *Geology* is the study of the _____.

6. A *pseudonym* is a _____ name.

7. A *biography* is a writing about a person's _____.

8. A *thermometer* is a _____ heat.

9. *Telestar* means "a _____ star."

10. A *telephone* produces _____ at a distance from the speaker.

D. What meaning does the prefix add in each word below? Write the meaning on the line provided.

1. misspell _____   6. intrastate _____

2. malpractice _____   7. interstate _____

3. hypertension _____   8. extraordinary _____

4. multilayered _____   9. foretell _____

5. precook _____   10. autograph _____

E. Complete each sentence by adding a word that fits in the blank space. Write this word on the line provided.

76

1. To postpone something is to set a _____ date for it. _____

2. An ultramodern house is _____ modern. _____

3. If someone is hypersensitive, he is _____ sensitive. _____

4. An extralegal act is one _____ what the law permits. _____

5. A minicamera is a _____ camera. _____

6. To forewarn someone is to warn him _____. _____

7. Intravenous feeding means putting liquid food _____ a vein. _____

8. A multivolume set of books has _____ volumes. _____

9. If a dog is maltreated, it is getting _____ treatment. _____

10. An autograph is a person's name written by _____. _____

Lesson 12.   Prefixes with More Than One Meaning

The prefixes you met in the last lesson have only one meaning. Other prefixes have two or three different meanings. When you find one of them in a word, you have to decide which of the meanings is at work. This is not very hard to do because the context provides clues.

There are a good many prefixes that we might consider, but we will deal here with only a few that occur frequently. They are worth special attention.

un
1) *not*: **un**known, **un**made, **un**married
2) *the opposite*: **un**tie, **un**wind, **un**bend

You can usually think of **un** as meaning "not," but there are some words in which "not" won't fit. In these words "the opposite" is the meaning. For example, to *untie* a package doesn't mean to not tie it. When you *untie* something, you do the opposite, or reverse, of something that was done before.

in
1) *not*: **in**correct, **in**active, **in**decent
2) *inside, within*: **in**born, **in**put, **in**ward

The difference between these two meanings is quite clear. There are many words beginning **in** in which neither meaning is at work: *injure, instant, insult,* for example.

The prefix **in** changes spelling in some words. It becomes **im** when added to a word beginning with **p**: **im**possible, **im**port. It also changes to **il** when the next letter is **l**: **il**legal and to **ir** when the next letter is **r**: **ir**religious. But the meanings of the prefix are the same despite the changed spelling.

dis
1) *away, apart*: **dis**card, **dis**charge, **dis**miss
2) *not*: **dis**honest, **dis**loyal
3) *the opposite*: **dis**obey, **dis**regard, **dis**prove

78

As you see, *dis* is like *un* in having the two meanings "not" and "the opposite." When *dis* is joined to a verb, it usually means "opposite": *to disobey* is the opposite of *to obey*. When *dis* is joined to an adjective, it usually means "not": *disloyal* means "not loyal." (If you can put *to* before a word, it is a verb. Thus you can say *to obey* but you can't say "to loyal.")

re
1) *back*: **re**turn, **re**pay, **re**bound
2) *again*: **re**paint, **re**fill, **re**form

ex
1) *out*: **ex**hale, **ex**haust, **ex**port
2) *former*: **ex**-convict, **ex**-President, **ex**-wife

When *ex* means "former," it is joined by a hyphen to the base word, as in the examples above.

anti
1) *against*: **anti**-Communist, **anti**war
2) *preventing, curing*: **anti**toxin, **anti**freeze

semi
1) *partly, somewhat*: **semi**conscious, **semi**skilled
2) *twice in a period*: **semi**weekly, **semi**monthly

sub
1) *beneath, below*: **sub**way, **sub**marine
2) *less than, somewhat*: **sub**normal, **sub**standard

TRY IT OUT

A. In which of the words below does *un* mean "not"? Write *yes* or *no*.

1. unknown _____   4. uneasy _____

2. unbind _____   5. unwrap _____

3. unwell _____   6. unsure _____

79

7. unkind _____ **9.** unable _____

8. unload _____ **10.** unafraid _____

B. In which of the words below does **un** mean "the opposite"? Write *yes* or *no*.

1. unwind _____ **6.** unbend _____

2. unclear _____ **7.** uncap _____

3. unpaid _____ **8.** unscrew _____

4. unseal _____ **9.** uncover _____

5. unbutton _____ **10.** unlock _____

C. In which of the words below does **in** mean "not"? In which does it mean "within, inside"? Remember the changes in spelling of the prefix. Write *not* or *within*.

1. inborn _____ **7.** indoor _____

2. input _____ **8.** inhuman _____

3. illegal _____ **9.** insane _____

4. include _____ **10.** invisible _____

5. inexact _____ **11.** ingrown _____

6. impossible _____ **12.** imprison _____

D. The prefix **dis** means (1) "away, apart," (2) "not," and (3) "the opposite." Decide which meaning it has in each word below. Write the meaning on the line provided.

1. disprove _____   6. distrustful _____

2. disagree _____   7. dislike _____

3. dismiss _____   8. dissatisfied _____

4. disband _____   9. disloyal _____

5. disobey _____   10. displace _____

E. One word is italicized in each sentence. What meaning does
    the prefix add to this word? Use the meanings listed on page
    79. Write the correct meaning on the line provided. The
    meaning of some of the stems is given in parentheses to help
    you. The first one is done for you.

1. The women *rejected* (threw) the manager's offer. ____*back*____

2. Ortiz *rejoined* the team in Atlanta. _____

3. Sarah *retells* the same stories over and over. _____

4. This smell *repels* (drives) the mosquitoes. _____

5. Sue was *reclining* (leaning) in her chair. _____

6. We *export* grain to many countries. _____

7. The *ex-governor* spoke at our meeting. _____

8. Cooking oil is *extracted* (drawn) from the peanuts. _____

9. The *ex-champion* is making a comeback. _____

10. In France the *antiwar* party was very strong. _____

11. Do you have an *antidote* for poison ivy? _____

12. Jerry put in another quart of *antifreeze.* _____

13. Her actions seem to be *antisocial.* _____

14. The new *antimalaria* drug is very effective. _____

15. The magazine comes out *semimonthly.* _____

16. The natives were only *semicivilized.* _____

17. At the hospital Tom had a *semiprivate* room. _____

18. A new *submarine* was launched yesterday. _____

19. The farmers were hurt by the *subnormal* rainfall. _____

20. The bargain counter is in the *subbasement.* _____

F. All three prefixes **dis**, **un**, and **in** (plus **im**, **in**, and **il**) can mean "not." Usually, only one of them can be added to a particular word. Decide which prefix you would add to each word below and write it on the line provided. The first one is done for you.

1. legal _____*il*_____   **8.** known _____

2. equal _____   **9.** possible _____

3. correct _____   **10.** direct _____

4. even _____   **11.** honorable _____

5. honest _____   **12.** exact _____

6. decided _____   **13.** legible _____

7. prepared _____   **14.** agreeable _____

15. washed   _____   **18.** active   _____

16. true   _____   **19.** steady   _____

17. skilled   _____   **20.** capable   _____

Lesson 13.   The Main Job of Suffixes

A suffix is a word part added at the end of a base word or stem: base*ment*, attrac*tion*.

Most English suffixes add little meaning to words. Their chief function is to show that a word belongs to a particular **word class** such as *nouns, verbs,* or *adjectives.* Each word class has a different job to do in a sentence. And usually a class of words occupies regular positions in a sentence.

By adding or by changing a suffix, we can change a word from one class to another. This lets us use a word in a different way in the sentence. And because it is used in a different way, it is moved to a different position. For example:

> As we went along, we got into a *thick* fog. (adjective)
> We could see the fog thick*en* as we went along. (verb)
> The thick*ness* of the fog increased. (noun)

> This book may *differ* from that one. (verb)
> There may be a differ*ence* between this book and that. (noun)
> This book may be differ*ent* from that. (adjective)

Since suffixes show which class a word belongs to, you would expect that any one suffix would be attached to just one class. In general, this is true, but a few suffixes are used for more than one class. For example, *y* is a suffix in both nouns (part*y*, honest*y*) and adjectives (dirt*y*, salt*y*). The suffix *al* appears in nouns (renew*al*, approv*al*) and in adjectives (fat*al*, usu*al*). But, mostly, a suffix is associated with just one word class.

Here is a list of the most common suffixes. Fix them in your memory because you will find them helpful in your reading.

Noun Suffixes	*Examples*
al	renew*al*, deni*al*
ance	import*ance*, alli*ance*
cy	infan*cy*, recen*cy*
ence	differ*ence*, influ*ence*
er	advis*er*, bowl*er*

ion	ac*tion*, correc*tion*
ist	pian*ist*, chem*ist*
ity	pur*ity*, formal*ity*
ment	govern*ment*, state*ment*
ness	kind*ness*, bright*ness*
or	act*or*, instruct*or*
ty	certain*ty*, safe*ty*
ure	pleas*ure*, depart*ure*
y	part*y*, honest*y*

Note: The suffix *ion* appears as **ation** in some words. When *ion* and **ation** are added to words ending *e*, the *e*, is dropped.

note + ation ⟶ not*ation*
accuse + ation ⟶ accus*ation*
vacate + ion ⟶ vaca*tion*
create + ion ⟶ crea*tion*

Verb Suffixes	*Examples*
ate	cre*ate*, nomin*ate*
en	length*en*, broad*en*
ify	glor*ify*, pur*ify*
ize	organ*ize*, burglar*ize*

Adjective Suffixes	*Examples*
al	form*al*, norm*al*
ant	pleas*ant*, ignor*ant*
en	wool*en*, wood*en*
ent	confid*ent*, differ*ent*
ful	care*ful*, use*ful*
ish	child*ish*, fool*ish*
ive	act*ive*, creat*ive*
ly	friend*ly*, home*ly*
ous	marvel*ous*, curi*ous*
y	dirt*y*, smok*y*

PUT IT TO WORK

A. Refer to the list of noun suffixes on pages 84-85. By adding one of these suffixes, change each word below to a noun. Write the new word. The first one is done for you.

1. major   _majority_   **11.** confer   _____

2. acquaint   _____   **12.** expose (drop *e*)   _____

3. broil   _____   **13.** astonish   _____

4. err   _____   **14.** annoy   _____

5. infect   _____   **15.** agree   _____

6. fail   _____   **16.** insist   _____

7. secure (drop *e*)   _____   **17.** arrive (drop *e*)   _____

8. adorn   _____   **18.** prevent   _____

9. allow   _____   **19.** entire   _____

10. frequent (drop *t*)   _____   **20.** dark   _____

B. Refer to the list of verb suffixes on page 85. Change each word or stem below to a verb by adding a verb suffix. Write the new word.

1. general   _____   **4.** note (drop *e*)   _____

2. test   _____   **5.** length   _____

3. elev   _____   **6.** commercial   _____

7. grat   _____   14. author   _____

8. magnet   _____   15. illustr   _____

9. terr   _____   16. solid   _____

10. terror   _____   17. tender   _____

11. heart   _____   18. light   _____

12. myst   _____   19. elimin   _____

13. strength   _____   20. threat   _____

C. Refer to the list of adjective suffixes on page 85. By adding one of these suffixes, change each word or stem below to an adjective. Write the new word.

1. year   _____   11. dust   _____

2. gold   _____   12. outland   _____

3. marvel   _____   13. confid   _____

4. book   _____   14. collect   _____

5. assert   _____   15. friend   _____

6. form   _____   16. child   _____

7. like   _____   17. love   _____

8. peril   _____   18. addition   _____

9. nation   _____   19. effect   _____

10. persist   _____   20. wind   _____

D. In the sentences below, the italicized words do not fit. You can make them fit by adding the right suffix. Choose one of the following suffixes and write the new word. The first one is done for you.

ance	ent	ish	ly	ness
en	ion	ize	ment	ous

1. He spoke in a *friend* way.   _____*friendly*_____

2. The state plans to *straight* the road here. _____

3. The police moved in to end the *disturb*. _____

4. The new boss is quite *differ* from the old one. _____

5. Dora's head felt *fever*. _____

6. The *announce* caught us by surprise. _____

7. The Olsens are very *neighbor*. _____

8. Maria's *alert* saved us from trouble. _____

9. Felipe's *suggest* was adopted at once. _____

10. Bill plans to *special* in electronic repairs. _____

11. The *entertain* starts at nine o'clock. _____

12. This crossing is very *danger*. _____

13. There is no question about Lincoln's *great*. _____

14. The *weak* of his argument was clear to everyone. _____

15. It's hard to *real* that the store is closing. _____

Lesson 14. Facing Up to Long Words

Remember this: No word is difficult just because it is long. Long words are usually made up of prefixes and suffixes joined to a base word or stem.

Find the base word or stem and you will have a good clue to the meaning. All you need the first time you meet an unfamiliar word is enough meaning to get on with your reading.

Let's look at a few examples to see how words can be broken down into their parts.

disorganization: dis/organiz/ation
    prefix: *dis*   base word: *organize*
    suffix: *ation*

collaboration: col/labor/ation
    prefix: *col*   base word: *labor*
    suffix: *ation*

accompaniment: ac/compani/ment
    prefix: *ac*   base word: *company*
    suffix: *ment*

Sometimes, there is a spelling change when a suffix is added. If you cut off the suffix, the remainder may look different from the base word that you know. The following spelling changes are important.

1. Final *e* (the *e* at the end of a word) is usually dropped when a suffix beginning with a vowel is added.

   eas*e* + *y* ⟶ easy
   organiz*e* + *ation* ⟶ organization

2. A *y* at the end of a word is called final *y*. If a consonant letter comes just before final *y*, the *y* usually changes to *i* when a suffix is added. The one big exception is that the *y* does not change when *ing* is added.

merry + ly ⟶ merrily
party + es ⟶ parties
hurry + ing ⟶ hurrying

If a vowel letter—*a*, *e*, *i*, *o*, or *u*—comes just before final *y*, the *y* does not change when a suffix is added.

enjoy + ment ⟶ enjoyment
employ + able ⟶ employable
employ + ing ⟶ employing

Frequently, when a suffix is added, there is a change in pronunciation, which must be taken into account in spelling.

1. Letters are dropped.

explain + ation ⟶ explanation
hunger + y ⟶ hungry
curious + ity ⟶ curiosity
infant + cy ⟶ infancy

2. Letters are added.

circle + ar ⟶ circular (also *e* is dropped)
possible + ity ⟶ possibility (also *e* is dropped)
act + al — actual
grade + ate ⟶ graduate (also *e* is dropped)

3. Letters are changed.

ai changed to *e*: detain + tion ⟶ detention
b changed to *p*: describe + tion ⟶ description
d changed to *t*: intend + ion ⟶ intention
d changed to *s*: decide + ive ⟶ decisive
e changed to *i*: college + ate ⟶ collegiate
t changed to *ss*: permit + ion ⟶ permission
v changed to *p*: receive + tion ⟶ reception (also *i* is dropped)

In breaking up a long word, you will often come to a Latin stem. Unfortunately, Latin stems have several different meanings, which show up in different English words. There is no way to be sure of which meaning occurs in a particular word. Yet, if you keep this in mind, some Latin words and stems will be helpful.

Word	Meaning	Example
manus	hand	manuscript
audio	hear	audience
bene	good, well	beneficial
corpus	body	corpulent
finis	end	final
gressus	step	progress
mortis	death	mortal
terminus	boundary, end	terminate
terra	earth	terrestrial

Stem	Meaning	Example
cred	believe	credible
fer	carry, bring	transfer
fid	faith	confide
ject	throw	reject
	place	inject
pel	drive	compel
	beat	repel
tract	draw	extract
	pull	tractor
vis	see	visible
	look after, see to	provide

One last word: In dealing with long, unfamiliar words, you will need all the skills and information you have acquired about context!

SEE FOR YOURSELF

A. In the following words, the spelling of the base word was changed when the suffix was added. Find the base word and write it on the line provided. The first one is done for you.

1. decorator	_decorate_	6. trial	_____
2. deciding	_____	7. mysterious	_____
3. pleasant	_____	8. apologist	_____
4. creation	_____	9. spicy	_____
5. approval	_____	10. carrier	_____

B. Try again. Several kinds of spelling changes occurred when suffixes were added in the following words. Find the base word and write it on the line provided.

1. exclamation	_____	11. deception	_____
2. singular	_____	12. maintenance	_____
3. graduate	_____	13. retention	_____
4. prevalent	_____	14. miraculous	_____
5. inscription	_____	15. frequency	_____
6. contention	_____	16. conclusion	_____
7. provision	_____	17. submission	_____
8. malicious	_____	18. perception	_____
9. racial	_____	19. liability	_____
10. commission	_____	20. obstinacy	_____

C. Add the suffix given and write the new word. You may have to add, drop, or change letters. The first one is done for you.

1. fact + al   _factual_   11. collide + ion   _____

2. intellect + al   _____   12. remit + ion   _____

3. contract + al   _____   13. suspend + ion   _____

4. detain + tion   _____   14. available + ity   _____

5. muscle + ar   _____   15. sustain + ance   _____

6. extend + ion   _____   16. finance + al   _____

7. frequent + cy   _____   17. retain + tion   _____

8. reveal + ation   _____   18. absorb + tion   _____

9. conceive + tion   _____   19. accurate + cy   _____

10. provide + ion   _____   20. minister + y   _____

D. Review the meanings of the Latin words and stems on page 91. Complete each sentence by providing the English word that expresses the meaning of the Latin stem in the italicized word. Write this word on the line provided. The first one is done for you.

1. *Manual* labor is work done with the _____ _hands_ _____.

2. A *manual* is a book of facts or instructions that can be held in the

_____.

3. In a tryout, or *audition*, performers are _____ by judges or

casting directors.

4. A *beneficial* action is one that produces some _____.

5. An act of *finality* brings uncertainty to an _____.

6. A *corps* is a _____ of people working together under common direction.

7. If a patient's health *regresses*, it _____ back.

8. When we speak of the *mortality* rate of a disease, we are referring to the _____ it causes.

9. The *termination* of a journey is its _____.

10. A *mortuary* is a place where the _____ are kept before burial or cremation.

11. *Corporal* punishment is inflicted upon the _____.

12. A *terrestrial* globe is one that represents the _____.

13. If you lack *confidence* in someone, you lack _____ in him.

14. An *incredible* statement is hard to _____.

15. An *extract* is something _____ out of something else.

16. To make *provision* for one's future is to _____ oneself.

17. If you make a *conjecture* about what happened, you _____ together what you know about it.

18. When you *retract* a statement, you _____ it back.

19. You _____ people together for a *conference*.

20. A *repellent* odor is one that _____ you back.

E. The meaning of each numbered sentence depends upon the meaning of the italicized word. Look for a familiar base word, and use the context and your knowledge of word parts to figure out that word. Three possible meanings are given for each sentence. Place an *x* on the line next to the correct one.

1. *Hospitalization* charges to patients have risen steadily because hospitals have had to install expensive new equipment.

   (a) The number of patients in hospitals has risen steadily. _____

   (b) Hospital patients have to pay more so that the hospitals can pay for new equipment. _____

   (c) Hospitalization means installing new equipment. _____

2. When Senator Baker's bill was finally passed by the Congress, it had been changed so much that he found it *unrecognizable*.

   (a) Senator Baker could not understand the bill that was finally passed. _____

   (b) In spite of the changes, Senator Baker believed that the bill was pretty much the same as the one he had proposed. _____

   (c) Senator Baker could see little likeness between his bill and the one finally passed. _____

3. Dalton's Department Store has announced the *discontinuation* of free delivery of purchases.

   (a) The store will not deliver purchases free any more. _____

   (b) The store will continue free delivery of purchases. _____

   (c) The announcement about free delivery has been stopped. _____

4. Some jobs call for *creativity*, but others require patient attention to details rather than the ability to come up with new ideas and different ways of doing things.

   (a) Creativity is the ability to attend to details patiently. _____

   (b) Creativity is the ability to create new ideas and different ways of doing things. _____

   (c) Creativity is the same thing as patient attention to detail. _____

5. Chess and checkers have much in common, but *basically* chess requires more study, more thought, and a better memory.

   (a) The chief difference between chess and checkers is the base on which they are built.   ——

   (b) When you get to the bottom of the two games, they are really alike.   ——

   (c) At bottom, chess requires more from the players than checkers does.   ——

Lesson 15.   Check Your Progress

You have met quite a number of word parts in the preceding lessons, and it may be difficult to keep them straight. Practice and experience with them will be helpful. Reread the introduction to the lessons. Try any device that you know for fixing things in your memory. Then turn to the practice below.

I. Find the correct meanings in the column on the right for the combining forms listed below. Write the number of the meaning on the line next to the combining form to which it belongs.

Combining Form *Meaning*

1. bio —— a. device for seeing, observing

2. geo —— b. sound

3. micro —— c. science or study

4. meter —— d. life

5. ology —— e. light

6. phono —— f. distance, distant

7. photo —— g. small

8. pseudo —— h. false

9. scope —— i. earth

10. tele —— j. device for measuring

97

II. Complete each sentence by supplying a word for the blank space. Write this word on the line provided at the right.

1. A *biography* is an account of a person's _____. _____

2. *Geography* is the study of the surface of the _____. _____

3. *Phonetics* is the study of the _____ of speech. _____

4. *Television* gives a view of something that is happening at a _____. _____

5. A *microprint* is a very _____ photograph of a printed page. _____

6. An alti*meter* is used in airplanes to _____ the distance from the plane to the ground. _____

7. A spectro*scope* is a device for _____ the series of colored bands in white light that pass through a prism. _____

8. Ec*ology* is the _____ of the effect of environment on living things. _____

9. A *photo*meter is a device for measuring the intensity of _____. _____

10. A *pseudo*scientist is someone who makes a _____ claim to being a scientist. _____

III. Complete each sentence by supplying the correct word or words that belong in the blank space. Write them on the line provided.

1. Anyone guilty of *malpractice* has been engaged in _____ practice. _____

2. A *miniature* painting is contained in a _____ area. _____

3. A *multicolored* coat is one of _____ colors. _____

98

4. If something is *extraordinary* it lies _____ the ordinary events of life.

_____

5. You *postdate* a check by writing in a date that is _____ than that of the day on which the check is written.

_____

6. To *misdirect* a letter is to put the _____ address on it.

_____

7. To *preview* a movie is to see it _____ it is shown generally.

_____

8. To be *forewarned* of a difficulty is to be warned _____ it comes up.

_____

9. A governmental agency that enjoys *autonomy* is _____ -governed.

_____

10. A *nonpartisan* group is one _____ supporting any one party.

_____

11. A *hypercritical* person offers _____ criticism.

_____

12. An *intrastate* bus line operates _____ one state.

_____

13. A player who *intercepts* a pass catches it _____ the passer and the intended receiver.

_____

14. Vibrations which are _____ the reach of the human ear are *ultrasonic*.

_____

IV. Decide which meaning of the prefix occurs in each word below. Write the meaning.

1. antimalaria _____ **6.** semiweekly _____

2. incomplete _____ **7.** prepay _____

3. inhale _____ **8.** subsoil _____

4. immoral _____ **9.** semisoft _____

5. antiaircraft _____ **10.** illegal _____

99

11. subhuman _____   16. disorderly _____

12. unapproved _____   17. disappear _____

13. disloyal _____   18. import _____

14. dismount _____   19. unwind _____

15. unequal _____   20. unwrap _____

V. The italicized words and stems do not fit in the sentences below. By adding the right suffix you can make them fit. Add the suffix and write the new word.

1. There was a *renew* of interest in building the bridge. _____

2. We could not be sure of his *ident*. _____

3. The plane turned back because of engine *fail*. _____

4. It was a *child* thing to do. _____

5. The change in her appearance was almost *magic*. _____

6. He has never held an *elect* office. _____

7. A *mystery* stranger appeared in town. _____

8. What can you say to *soft* the blow? _____

9. Will you please *note* us when you ship the goods. _____

10. Kate plans to *special* in electronic repairs. _____

VI. Add the suffix given and write the new word.

1. maintain + ance _____   2. perceive + tion _____

3. divide + ion _____

4. recent + cy _____

5. commerce + al _____

6. muscle + ar _____

7. liable + ity _____

8. hunger + y _____

9. attend + ion _____

10. commit + ion _____

VII. The Latin stem is italicized in each word below. Figure out
what meaning it adds to the word. Write the meaning.

1. *man*ual _____

2. *audi*tory _____

3. *cred*ulous _____

4. *bene*factor _____

5. *fid*elity _____

6. in*ject*ion _____

7. dis*tract*ion _____

8. in*corp*orate _____

9. *term*inal _____

10. pro*vis*ion _____

11. con*fine* _____

12. *terri*tory _____

13. dis*pel* _____

14. re*ject*ion _____

15. di*gress*ion _____

16. con*fer*ence _____

17. ex*tract*ion _____

18. *mort*ality _____

19. con*fid*ence _____

20. im*pel* _____

VIII. Find the base word or stem in each long word below.
Write it on the line provided. Be on guard for spelling
changes.

1. unrealistic _____

2. discontinuous _____

3. revaluation   ———————   **7.** immaturity   ———————

4. incredible   ———————   **8.** unresponsive   ———————

5. unsystematic   ———————   **9.** prehistoric   ———————

6. distraction   ———————   **10.** reforestation   ———————

Midway Check

You have learned a great deal about word meanings, word parts, and context. You have discovered how prefixes, suffixes, and context clues can lead you to the meaning of an unfamiliar word. What you have learned thus far will help you in the lessons to follow. How much do you remember?

I. Find the clues to the meaning of the italicized words. Some of them are signal words and others are modifiers. Underline the words that give the clues.

1. The federal government has granted several billion dollars for *urban renewal programs*, such as repairing or rebuilding houses, tearing down slum areas, and installing sewerage systems.

2. *Zero population growth* means a birthrate that just replaces but does not increase population.

3. *Recycling*, especially reuse of paper and metal, will help preserve our resources of forests and minerals.

4. There was always a shortage of *specie*, copper, gold, and silver coins, in this country until gold and silver were discovered in the West.

5. Much of our food is harvested by *migrant workers*, moving from one part of the country to another as crops mature.

6. Most young people belong to several *peer groups*, that is, groups of people of their own age.

7. Some chemical elements can be identified by a *flame test*, in which a small portion placed in a flame burns with a distinctive color.

8. Isabel works as a *paramedic*, taking temperatures, blood pressures, and pulse rates, so that the doctor can spend his time on diagnosis and treatment.

9. The children will inherit the property when they reach their *majority*, the age at which they have full rights and responsibilities of an adult.

10. The machinery was not *impaired*; that is, it was not damaged.

II. Find the connector in each sentence and underline it. Decide what relationship it signals. Write *cause*, *effect*, *time*, or *contrast*.

1. I didn't see him leave, although I was standing at the door. _____

2. The orders to move were definite; accordingly, we left the next day. _____

3. We were just about to leave when you telephoned. _____

4. The chances for success are not good; nonetheless, we are going ahead with our plans. _____

5. Harriet could not cash the check since she had no identification with her. _____

6. While the instructions were very detailed, they still left several questions unanswered. _____

7. Everyone knows some heavy smoker who has had lung cancer; yet, there is no decline in cigarette smoking. _____

8. Rents have gone up fast since the first of the year. _____

9. The line at the box office was very long; however, it was moving fast. _____

10. Helen had to wait an hour because she had been late for her appointment. _____

III. In each sentence one word is italicized. Three meanings are given for this word. Find the meaning that fits. Place an *x* on the line next to it.

1. In the middle of the summer, interest in the project *languished*.

   (a) lost vigor and force _____

   (b) lived in distress and suffering _____

   (c) suffered from longing for _____

2. As we neared the hospital, Judy *lapsed* into unconsciousness.

   (a) came to an end _____

   (b) fell into error _____

   (c) fell into a state of _____

3. The women were *flushed* with their success in the election.

   (a) red in the face _____

   (b) excited and encouraged _____

   (c) cleaned out with a flow of water _____

4. Jerry spent a *solid* month replacing the engine.

   (a) firm, strong, and substantial _____

   (b) serious _____

   (c) without pause or interruption _____

5. The new manager was given wide *latitude* in running his department.

   (a) distance north or south of the equator _____

   (b) freedom of action _____

   (c) area _____

6. Many of our foods are *fortified* with vitamins by the manufacturer.

(a) enriched   _____

(b) protected against spoiling   _____

(c) made more palatable   _____

7. The employer is *liable* for any injury suffered by a worker because of faulty equipment.

(a) likely to be   _____

(b) subject to   _____

(c) legally responsible   _____

8. The owner of the plant assured the reporter that he *harbored* no ill will toward the strikers.

(a) tied to the dock   _____

(b) held   _____

(c) sheltered   _____

9. The supervisor *tempered* her criticism of Jessie by praising the quality of her work.

(a) made less harsh   _____

(b) hardened   _____

(c) strengthened   _____

10. The chairman of the committee has *discharged* his duties quickly and efficiently.

(a) dismissed   _____

(b) performed   _____

(c) released from a burden   _____

IV. Find the clues to the meaning of the italicized word or phrase in each paragraph. Three definitions of the italicized word or phrase follow each paragraph. Place an *x* next to the correct definition.

1. Members of the House and Senate are always reluctant to bring charges of improper or criminal conduct against their colleagues. It takes an aroused and indignant public to move them to begin a committee investigation. There is less reluctance to challenge judges or members of the executive branch, and Congress has done so on several occasions. The Constitution provides that the House has the sole power to *impeach* a public official for "treason, bribery, or high crime and misdemeanor." The Senate is empowered to try the cases of those against whom charges are brought. That is, the House acts as prosecutor and grand jury; the Senate acts as judge and trial jury.

To *impeach* means to

(a) try an official for an alleged crime ____

(b) charge an official with having committed a crime ____

(c) convict an official of criminal action ____

2. Sarah's early years were not disturbed by *sibling rivalry*. She had no sisters with whom she might be compared. Her only brother was born when Sarah was 12 and was always more of a pet than a competitor.

Sibling rivalry means

(a) taking care of another member of the family ____

(b) being an only child ____

(c) competing with brothers or sisters ____

3. In every local government there is an official who has the job of deciding the value of land and buildings owned by the taxpayers. This is the *assessor*. This estimate of what a property is worth is used by other officials who set the taxes to be paid. In some places property is assessed at its full value; in others, at only part of its value. Whatever method is used, the assessor must apply it evenly to all properties in the district.

An *assessor*

(a) decides how much tax is to be paid on a property ____

(b) advises people on how much to pay for a house ____

(c) decides the value of land and buildings for purposes of taxation ____

4. Jack's record in making important choices was not a good one. He had a *propensity* for making bad decisions. For instance, he dropped out of high school when he might have continued. Later, he trained as a printer only to find that no jobs were available, and he married a girl who gave him constant trouble until she divorced him.

Propensity means

(a) a natural tendency ____

(b) inability to make a decision ____

(c) a great talent or gift ____

V. The prefix or the combining form is italicized in each word. What meaning does it add to the word? Write the meaning on the line provided.

1. *im*polite _____

2. *re*ject _____

3. *micro*wave _____

4. thermo*meter* _____

5. *tele*star _____

6. *pseudo*nym _____

7. *mal*practice _____

8. *mis*informed _____

9. *dis*agree _____

10. eco*logy* _____

11. *extra*ordinary _____

12. *intra*muscular _____

13. *im*bedded _____

14. *hyper*sensitive _____

15. *anti*knock _____

16. *un*tie _____

17. *in*grown _____

18. *dis*place _____

19. *re*state   _____   **22.** *ex*hale   _____

20. *semi*monthly   _____   **23.** *sub*cellar   _____

21. *sub*human   _____   **24.** *ultra*sonic   _____

VI. The italicized words do not fit in the sentences below. By adding the right suffix, you can make them fit. Add the suffix and write the new word.

1. Will Dr. Brown accept the *nominate*?   _____

2. It was a *child* thing to do.   _____

3. The *depart* of the bus was delayed.   _____

4. I was glad to make her *acquaint*.   _____

5. This wallpaper will *bright* the room.   _____

6. The gang began to *terror* the neighborhood.   _____

7. What is the *national* of these tourists?   _____

8. The mixture will *solid* in a few minutes.   _____

9. It is a very *attract* house.   _____

10. The *quick* of the decision delighted us.   _____

VII. Face up to the long words below. By dropping prefixes and suffixes, find the base word in each long word below. Write it on the line provided. Watch for spelling changes.

1. unresponsive   _____   **3.** ineffectiveness   _____

2. impermissible   _____   **4.** migratory   _____

5. modernization   _____

6. necessitating   _____

7. orchestration   _____

8. revelatory   _____

9. systematized   _____

10. interminable   _____

11. suggestibility   _____

12. unpretentious   _____

13. unrealistic   _____

14. impressionable   _____

Lesson 16. Words Don't Always Mean What They Say

Most words in everyday use have several meanings. Usually, there is some connection between the meanings so that you can see how one grew out of another. Occasionally, there is a meaning entirely unrelated, even opposite, to the others.

Knowing these facts about words, you do not expect a word to have the same meaning in every sentence. But in some expressions and phrases, *none* of the usual meanings seems to fit. The phrase has a special meaning of its own. Phrases of this sort are called **idioms**. You cannot get the meaning of the phrase by adding together the meaning of each of the words within it.

For example, if someone says, "Put out the cat," you add the meanings from left to right *put* + *out* + *the* + *cat*. Then, you pick up the cat and place (put) it outside (out). But if someone asks you to *put out the light*, you don't pick up the light and put it anywhere. In "put out the cat," each word has its usual meaning. In "put out the light," the words *put out* have a special meaning. They are an idiom.

Many American idioms are made by adding a verb such as *put* to an adverb such as *out*. In some sentences, however, the words *out*, *in*, *up*, *down*, etc., are not necessary to the meaning. They are used as space fillers (brush *off* your coat) or for emphasis (Hurry *up*).

Another kind of idiom is the *common expression*, which may be made up of words from any word class. Each of these expressions has a clear and definite meaning in American English; for example:

a shot in the dark   blow off steam
on the level   blow hot and cold

Some of these expressions are *slang*, which suddenly sweeps the country and just as quickly vanishes. Some slang stays on, performing a useful purpose, and becomes a respectable part of the language. In a slang expression the words seldom have their usual meanings. The meaning lies in the expression as a whole.

111

An expression may start out in one particular sport or occupation, with each word having its ordinary meaning. When the expression is carried over into other situations, the usual meanings of the words no longer apply. Thus, a *ten-strike* in bowling means that all ten pins are struck down by one ball. Carried over into other situations, it means "a great success." *To hit the jackpot* means "to get the largest sum paid out by a slot machine." In ordinary affairs it means "to win or gain a lot of money." When such expressions are moved out of their regular setting, the words lose their regular meanings. *The expression as a whole has a meaning of its own.*

If you were born in this country or if you have lived here a long time, these idioms are not difficult. They are interesting because they show how words can be used with little regard for their usual meanings. The important thing is to realize when this is happening.

TRY THESE

A. In which sentences is the italicized word necessary for the meaning? Try saying the sentences without these words. Write *yes* or *no*. The first one is done for you.

1. She backed *up* the truck into the alley.   <u>*no*</u>

2. The doctor stopped to light *up* his pipe.   _____

3. Please write *down* your name on this paper.   _____

4. Inez showed *up* very well on the test.   _____

5. This is a good day for washing *off* the car.   _____

6. Pablo nearly fell *off* the stool.   _____

7. I hate to give *in* to a cold.   _____

8. Will you please continue *on* with the story?   _____

9. They kept right *on* working until midnight. _____

10. Gwendolyn Brooks grew *up* in Chicago. _____

11. Check *off* the names of those who are present. _____

12. The fair will end *up* on Friday. _____

13. We expect you to carry *out* the plans. _____

14. Let's clear *off* this table. _____

15. He fell *down* on the porch. _____

16. The band was coming *down* the street. _____

17. Wipe *off* the glasses. _____

18. It rained *down* hard all day. _____

19. They filled *up* the holes with stones. _____

20. The parents entered *in* the games. _____

B. In which sentences are the italicized words an idiom? Write *yes* or *no*. The first one is done for you.

1. We *came across* an old friend from Pittsburgh. *yes*

2. The men *came* directly *across* the field. _____

3. They *went, after* the first act. _____

4. The crowd *went after* the hecklers with fists and stones. _____

5. What has *come over* you lately? _____

6. *Bring* the typewriter *up* to the third floor. _____

7. I will *bring up* the matter at the next meeting. _____

8. She *came through* the experience very well. _____

9. She is an easy person to *get along* with. _____

10. See if you can *get around* to the back of the house. _____

11. This is one fact you can't *get around*. _____

12. Sue stood on tiptoe to *look over* the wall. _____

13. I *looked through* the papers for your advertisement. _____

14. You can't *see through* the windows. _____

15. Unless we get a loan, the business will *go under*. _____

16. The color doesn't *go with* her complexion. _____

17. We will *go with* Mr. Washington as far as Trenton. _____

18. We saw two people *down on* the pier. _____

19. He thinks the teacher is *down on* him. _____

20. It is hard to *make out* the name. _____

C. Are you sure you know the meaning of the common expressions which appear in italics below? Three possible meanings are given for each expression. Decide which is correct and place an **x** on the line next to it.

1. The lawyer's question was just *a shot in the dark*.

  (a) disturbing _____

  (b) without a definite aim _____

  (c) unexpected _____

2. It's *six of one and half a dozen of another.*

    (a) it amounts to the same thing   _____

    (b) a total of twelve   _____

    (c) not very clear   _____

3. The witness who accused George of embezzlement was *tarred with the same brush.*

    (a) covered with tar   _____

    (b) not to be believed   _____

    (c) guilty of the same crime   _____

4. Maggie's arguments *struck home* with the committee.

    (a) hurt the committee's feelings   _____

    (b) made no impression   _____

    (c) had a strong effect   _____

5. The supervisor *took* the women *to task* for their sloppy work.

    (a) assigned an extra task as punishment   _____

    (b) made their tasks harder   _____

    (c) scolded   _____

6. By digging out the facts, the minority, who wanted the new charter, *turned the tables* on the opposition.

    (a) moved the tables around   _____

    (b) secured an advantage over   _____

    (c) angered   _____

7. There is trouble *in store for* the clerks who did not get to work on Saturday.

    (a) in stock   _____

(b) somewhere in the store _____

(c) awaiting _____

8. We bought the car *on the strength of* your recommendation.

(a) in reliance on _____

(b) on credit _____

(c) with the help of _____

9. The editor agreed that the Senator should be criticized, but she hesitated to *cast the first stone.*

(a) make a public statement _____

(b) attack viciously _____

(c) begin the criticism _____

10. The result of the election *hangs in the balance.*

(a) is not settled _____

(b) is hung up by delays _____

(c) is being weighed against something else _____

11. The commissioner let the protesters *cool their heels* outside her office.

(a) take off their shoes _____

(b) wait a long time _____

(c) sit in comfortable chairs _____

12. When the players presented their idea, the coach *chimed in.*

(a) answered _____

(b) disagreed _____

(c) agreed _____

13. Dan said he would go on the ski trip, but at the last minute he *got cold feet.*

(a) became afraid to go   _____

(b) caught a cold in his feet   _____

(c) froze his feet   _____

14. He is a hard man to work for, but *give the devil his due,* he is usually fair.

(a) give an evil man the punishment he deserves   _____

(b) pay an evil man what you owe him   _____

(c) admit that the evil man has his good points   _____

15. When Vera lost her job, it was hard for her to *make both ends meet.*

(a) to touch her toes   _____

(b) to tie things together   _____

(c) to keep expenses within her income   _____

D. The common expressions at the left should be familiar to you. From the list at the right, find the meaning of the expression. Write its letter on the line provided. The first one is done for you.

Expression		*Meaning*
1. make no bones about it	_e_	(a) don't disturb things or something worse might happen
2. have a bone to pick with	___	(b) something sudden and unexpected
3. dress down	___	(c) a tie
4. brush up on	___	(d) be undecided about

117

5. can't get to first base   ____   (e) make no attempt to hide

6. dead heat   ____   (f) have a cause for complaint

7. a bolt from the blue   ____   (g) avoid getting to the point

8. beat around the bush   ____   (h) scold severely

9. blow hot and cold   ____   (i) can't even make a start in getting something done

10. let sleeping dogs lie   ____   (j) review

More Than One Meaning

Some idioms have several meanings. *Pick up* is a good example. The ordinary meaning is "to grasp and lift with the hands or fingers." But used as an idiom, *pick up* may mean

1. to get or learn something by chance (pick up information, pick up a bargain)
2. to stop for and bring along (pick up the groceries)
3. to arrest (pick up a suspect)
4. to move faster (pick up speed)
5. to improve (business picked up)
6. to make neat (pick up a room)

There are still other meanings that may occur to you.

Lesson 17. Literal and Figurative Language

Some people think of figurative language as belonging solely to poetry. Nothing could be further from the truth. Figurative language is a natural way of expression that we use constantly to express our feelings and attitudes and to express them forcefully. We say:

> I wouldn't be caught dead in that place.
> That's the worst thing you could do.
> It will cost you an arm and a leg.

These are **exaggerations**. They overstate the case. They are, in short, **figurative language**, used to decorate our speech, to make it more forceful and lively.

Why *figurative*? One meaning of *figure* is "the outline of something." An outline of a house suggests something about it but does not give the details necessary to identify it. Another meaning of *figure* is "decoration," like the figure in a piece of cloth. Figurative language does not give accurate details, and it is decorative.

If you say, "The experience was like a bad dream," you are not just reporting a fact; you are suggesting something about the experience. And you do it by using *like* to make a comparison. The word *as* is also used to make comparisons: "tough as shoe leather," "smooth as silk."

Two kinds of figurative language require special attention. The first is called **reifying** (re′i•fy•ing). Since the Latin stem *re* meant "thing," you might translate reifying as "thingifying." That is, in reifying we give physical character to something that does not exist physically:

> We *tossed* the *idea* back and forth.
> The *argument* is *full of holes*.
> It was an *empty promise*.

119

An idea is not something solid like a ball. Moths can eat holes in a woolen skirt, but not in an argument. You can see that a box is empty, but you can't see a promise.

The second kind of figurative language is called **personifying** (per•son'i•fy•ing). This is the giving of human character to a nonhuman thing.

> The *White House reports* that employment is rising.
> The *company is worried* about the drop in business.
> Your *office called* this morning.

The White House is a building, and a building cannot report. The president of a company can worry, but a company cannot. The questions for the reader or listener are

> Just who in the White House is reporting?
> Who in the company is worried? the clerks? the truck drivers? the president?
> Who in the office called? the boss? a friend?

When we want to report facts, to describe things as they really are, we use **literal language**. This is the language of science, of medicine, of the law, and of any other speech or writing that must be exact and free from exaggeration or decoration.

In literal language, words are used with their ordinary meanings. Human qualities are not given to things such as *office* and *company*; physical traits are not given to abstract things such as *opportunity* or *silence*. For example:

> The forecast is for rain tomorrow.
> It is now one minute before midnight.
> The power failure lasted for two hours.

These statements state the plain facts, at least as the writer knows them. The words do not suggest or state the feelings or attitudes of the writer. The words are used with their ordinary meanings.

It is important in getting meaning from what is said and written to be able to tell the difference between literal and figurative language. With a literal statement, you are expected to take the words for what they say. Figurative language says either more or less than what is really the case.

IT'S YOUR TURN

A.   Which of the following statements are literal and which are figurative? Write **L** for literal and **F** for figurative. The first one is done for you.

1. This is a difficult test.   <u>**L**</u>

2. It was a backbreaking job.   ____

3. The Governor's office has made no comment.   ____

4. She was puffing like a steam engine.   ____

5. The Giants won a lopsided victory over the Vikings.   ____

6. The valley was blanketed in fog.   ____

7. The officer found a key in the woman's handbag.   ____

8. The plant says it has no jobs available.   ____

9. The outcome of the election was uncertain.   ____

10. The ticket taker gave us a stony glance.   ____

11. His hat was too small and his coat was too long.   ____

12. The gates will be open at one o'clock.   ____

13. The Dodgers blasted the Yankees in the first game.   ____

14. The treasurer reports that we have a surplus.   ____

15. The company says that it is losing money.   ____

16. The terrorists were armed to the teeth.   ____

17. The heat in the desert was murderous.   ____

18. He ran the team with a sharp tongue and an iron hand.   ____

19. We were bowled over by the news.   _____

20. The bridge has been closed for repairs.   _____

B. Try again. Decide which statements are figurative and which are literal. Write *L* for literal and *F* for figurative.

1. After Lincoln's death, rumors popped up everywhere.   _____

2. We did not realize how late it was.   _____

3. The playing field was a sea of mud.   _____

4. Opposition to the plan melted away.   _____

5. The office wants this work done today.   _____

6. Bill let the opportunity float past him.   _____

7. The temperature was 82 degrees at eight o'clock.   _____

8. I could have bitten my tongue off.   _____

9. The story appeared in the late afternoon papers.   _____

10. The bank is not willing to give us a loan.   _____

11. The railroads ignored the needs of the farmers.   _____

12. Congress passed laws to regulate the railroad companies.   _____

13. We could see nothing beyond the headlights.   _____

14. Her silence tells us a great deal.   _____

15. You couldn't see your hand before your face.   _____

16. Fear of failure weighed heavily on his mind.   _____

17. All of the evidence was against him.   _____

18. The evidence pointed to his guilt.   _____

19. The runner stumbled and couldn't get to first base.   _____

20. You won't get to first base with that story.   _____

C. All of the following statements are figurative. For each one, decide what kind it is. Write *exaggeration*, *personifying*, or *reifying*. (Reread pages 119-20 to review what these terms mean.)

1. It was a golden opportunity. _____

2. The time flew past. _____

3. The White House reported the President's illness. _____

4. They had the audience rolling in the aisles. _____

5. The criticism, we thought, was quite shallow. _____

6. The administration favors an increase in taxes. _____

7. The post office refused to accept the packages. _____

8. The company is laughing at its competitors. _____

9. The radio says there were no survivors. _____

10. You have never heard such applause. _____

11. The ship announced its departure with four long blasts. _____

12. Her memory raced back to the day of the accident. _____

13. The price of gasoline immediately soared. _____

14. The party was a disaster. _____

15. You could have fried an egg on the sidewalk. _____

16. The attendance smashed all records. _____

17. His heart told him he was wrong. _____

18. You could have heard a pin drop. _____

19. It turned out to be a broken promise. _____

20. He turned the matter over in his mind. _____

What Kind of Mind Do You Have?

Long ago people invented the concept of *mind* as the doer and receiver of all mental activity. The mind does not exist physically. It has no size, no length, depth, or breadth. But observe how we speak of it:

keep something *in* mind

lose one's mind

be of *two* minds

have a *good* mind to

give someone a *piece* of one's mind

put one's mind on something

on one's mind

change one's mind

broad-minded

have *half* a mind to

take one's mind *off* something

make up one's mind

be *in* one's *right* mind

out of one's mind

In all of these expressions we speak *as if* the mind were something we could be in or out of, something that could be divided or doubled. It is *as if* the mind could be lost, made up, changed, or put on or off something. This is figurative language. This is **reifying**.

Lesson 18.   Suggested Meaning

On an ocean freighter, the captain and the first mate took turns in writing up the ship's log, or daily record. Relations between the two men were sometimes unpleasant, and after a particularly stormy day, the mate was dismayed to read in the captain's last entry: "The first mate was drunk last night." The mate thought this over and then in his turn wrote: "The captain was not drunk last night."

What he wrote was one thing: what he suggested was another.

In writing, as in speech, there is often a suggested meaning that the reader must catch. To miss it may be to miss the main point of what the writer is saying. *Suggested meaning* is part of the total meaning of a passage.

If someone says, "It seems warm in here," he may be suggesting that the heat be turned down or the window opened. If one woman asks another, "Where did you get that dress?" she may be suggesting that the dress is especially attractive.

It is particularly important to watch for the attitude of the writer toward the subject. The writer's attitude—feelings or beliefs about the subject—are part of the total meaning even though it is not stated in so many words. If it is not stated, the reader must "read between the lines" to dig it out. Let's look at two examples.

1. Several years have passed since Americans first became alarmed enough about their environment to do something about it. They have stopped burning leaves and trash. They have been using unleaded gas in their cars. Industrial plants are dumping less waste into rivers and lakes and much less noxious smoke into the air. Has anything happened as a result? Yes, the air is cleaner around New York, for example. People and fish are returning to waters which were once unsafe. In fact so much progress has been made that it is now being suggested that we can afford to let up a little and permit industrial plants to go back to their old ways. Before we agree to do so, we might consider the recent case of Love Valley, a community near Niagara Falls. The strange illnesses of the residents and

the number of their babies born with deformities have been traced to industrial wastes dumped into the ground by nearby industries years ago.

Does the writer favor "letting up"?
Does the writer say so?

2. Reading scores of high school students have been declining for several years. Colleges are spending increasing time and money to bring the basic skills of entering students to the level required for college work. Colleges, parents, and taxpayers have joined in placing the blame for this sorry state upon the schools. The schools, they say, have failed. But it is just possible that the schools are not solely to blame and that students and their parents may also be involved. Basic skills are not acquired just by sitting in a classroom.

Does the writer place all the blame on the schools?
Does the writer say that the schools are not to be blamed at all?
Does the writer believe that students and parents must share the blame?
Does the writer say so in so many words?

TRY IT OUT

A. Look for the suggested meaning, the belief or feeling that is not stated. Read the paragraphs carefully. Then mark the statements that follow each paragraph *true* or *false*.

1. When terrorists read about the capture of a few of their kind, they yawn and turn the page. They note that the captives are well treated. If they are placed on trial the judge and the jury will be threatened. If the culprits are convicted and sentenced, they will be sentenced to jail terms, not to death, and they can expect to be released through other acts of violence. Terrorists do not give their victims the choice of death or imprisonment. So long as they face no threat to their own lives if they are captured, we will continue to read of the kidnapping and murder of businessmen, political figures, and ambassadors.

(a) The writer believes that terrorists are not afraid of capture and court trial. _____

(b) The writer is opposed to giving terrorists the right to trial by jury. _____

(c) The writer believes that convicted terrorists should be put to death. _____

2. You can say this about Americans—that they are health conscious. They spend about as much on health remedies as they do on cigarettes and liquor. They buy carloads of books about this diet or that and read them carefully with a box of pretzels and a can of beer to help them through the pages. Or they are seized with a frenzy and stop eating essential foods altogether. They go faithfully to an exercise class one day a week, but on the other six days their chief exercise is getting in and out of bed. Or they take up jogging and stumble lonesomely along the side of a highway until they begin to notice irregular heartbeats. Yes sir, we Americans certainly try to take care of our health.

(a) The writer is praising the efforts of Americans to take care of their health. _____

(b) The writer is critical of diets and exercise. _____

(c) The writer is poking fun at the way Americans go about health care. _____

3. The play that opened at the Rex Theater last evening is advertised as "modern entertainment for modern audiences." If you like noise and commotion on the stage, you ought to see it. If following a plot is too much trouble, you will like this show. If what used to be prized as good acting is no longer the thing, this is indeed "modern entertainment." Unfortunately, I can't write a review of the play because I left before the first act was finished.

(a) The critic thinks that plot and good acting are not important in a play. _____

(b) The critic is condemning the play. _____

(c) The critic advises the reader to expect a lot of noise but not a plot or good acting. _____

B. Try again. Watch for the writer's suggested meaning that is not stated in so many words. Then mark the statements that follow each paragraph *true* or *false*.

1. Many people suffer from some form of extreme anxiety. Some experience occasional attacks of panic for no apparent reason. Others go around in a state of continual uneasiness. The usual way of controlling anxiety is with drugs, which cure none of the conditions described but do help patients manage their anxiety. Patients who take these drugs say that they are able to work, to sleep, and to go places they had feared to visit. But the effects of the drugs on the human body, especially on the nervous system, have been unknown....

We have started a series of studies to identify the effects of the drugs on the brain and have gained some insight into the costs and benefits of the antianxiety drugs. They are valuable because they can reduce the effects of anticipated failure, frustration, and disappointment. But their value demands a price. Two effects of the drugs are obviously harmful. They reduce a person's ability to react to changes in the environment; and more important, they keep a person from developing persistence in the face of unexpected troubles. Since it is fairly sure that people will meet problems they had not expected, this effect may make the price of antianxiety drugs too high.

(a) The writer opposes the use of antianxiety drugs.   _____

(b) The writer believes that the drugs have beneficial effects.   _____

(c) The writer believes that the bad effects of the drugs may
    outweigh their advantages.   _____

2. In all fairness to man it ought to be said that animals have had the advantage of an early start. Some were accomplished builders in time so remote as to defy the imagination. Termites, for example, have been around for more than 300 million years. Compared to them, man is no more than a straggler in the building field. Yet such is his conceit that he does not blush to compare the termites' construction to his own....

Unlike us, termites work without tools. They need no T square, saw, hammer, or chisel. The upper jaw serves them as a trowel, the antennae as rulers. Furthermore, their workers are quite blind. The curious thing is the phenomenal durability of their constructions, which by far exceed that of our houses. To wit, a large mound near Salisbury in Rhodesia, having been submitted to the most exacting tests, owned up to its age of 700 years....

One mound may house as many as 3 million termites. But unlike us, termites are passionately devoted to the common weal. They have been practicing socialism—under a queen be it noted—an infinity of time before its doctrine was formulated by man. They distinguish themselves by their social behavior, which is more than can be said for the human race.

(a) The writer thinks that humans are poor builders. _____

(b) The writer believes that humans have little reason to look down upon termites. _____

(c) The writer is criticizing human society by comparing it unfavorably to termite society. _____

(d) The writer believes that buildings constructed by humans do not last 700 years. _____

3. The Assay Office in New York City, a branch of the U.S. Mint, reported yesterday that $1.1 million in gold is missing from its vaults. The gold seems to have disappeared sometime between 1973 and 1977, and it may have been stolen or may have been lost as dust, the Assay Office states. Treasury officials in Washington "suggest"—that is their word—that the New York office may just have made a mistake in arithmetic in figuring out how much gold it should have on hand. The reported loss, they say, is barely 0.01 percent of the gold normally held in the Assay Office and such loss could be expected in the process of refining.

Shucks, what's a million dollars in other people's money? And who would expect a branch of the Treasury to make a count of its stock more often than once in four years? But maybe the Assay Office should shake out its vacuum cleaner more often. Maybe it should hire someone who can do simple sums in arithmetic. Or maybe it should put padlocks on its doors.

(a) The writer is defending the Assay Office. _____

(b) The writer is critical of the Assay Office. _____

(c) The writer believes that the loss of $1.1 million in gold is not important. _____

Lesson 19.   Seeing the Writer's Purpose

Language is always used for a purpose. It is always intended to do something *for* the speaker or *to* the listener.

It may be used to break an embarrassing silence: "Why doesn't someone say something?" It may just be an act of courtesy or friendliness. When people ask, "How are you today?" the last thing they want to hear is a catalogue of your aches and pains. When someone remarks, "It's a nice day, isn't it?" he or she is neither reporting the weather nor asking for information.

These are social uses of language. Their purpose is to acknowledge the presence of other people or to make contact with them. They are important in making everyday life agreeable and pleasant.

Perhaps you have heard someone carrying on a constant chatter about trivial matters. What is the purpose of this talk? Sometimes it is a deliberate effort to avoid serious matters that the speaker doesn't want brought up. Sometimes it is a way of relieving the speaker's tension. Some incessant talkers seem to fear that they may be ignored or forgotten in a period of silence. These are not very serious uses of language.

Among the important uses of language, the following seem to be the most common:

1. to give or get information
2. to express feelings
3. to arouse feelings in others
4. to get someone to do something
5. to get someone to believe something
6. to entertain or amuse
7. to hide or confuse meaning

It is important to keep in mind that the purpose of the speaker or writer is part of the meaning. If you consider only the words spoken without taking their purpose into account, you may be misled into a belief or action that you will regret.

A single statement or question may have just one purpose, as when you say:

What time is it? (to secure information)
It has started to rain. (to give information)

But any one of the purposes listed above can be combined with one or more of the others. For example:

When does this stupid program begin? (to secure information *and* to express feelings)
This car is the best buy for you because it gets 35 miles to a gallon of gas. (to give information *and* to get the listener to buy)
If you believe that the sick and elderly should not be abandoned by our government, you will support this bill. (to arouse feelings *and* to get someone to do something)

The most dangerous use of language is for the purpose of hiding or confusing meaning. When people reply to questions by making remarks that are off the subject, they are using language to confuse. If a writer quotes only part of someone's statement, the meaning of the original statement may be completely distorted.

This sort of thing happens in business. It happens in the ordinary affairs of family life as well as in public affairs and politics. The purpose of the writer or speaker is as important as the words being used. The purpose may be honest and reasonable —you don't have to be suspicious of everything—but it may also be something to your disadvantage.

DO IT YOURSELF

A. Find two purposes for the language in each item below. Choose from the words and phrases that follow. Write your answers on the lines provided. (You will find two purposes given in the key, but you may find more than two yourself.)

inform   arouse feelings   get to believe
express feelings   get to do   amuse

131

1. Emergency Parking Only (a highway sign)

   _____

   _____

2. Buy now and pay later on our easy-payment plan. You can make monthly payments over a two-year period if you wish. Interest charges on your unpaid balance come to only 12% on an annual basis. And you can avoid even this reasonable charge by paying up the balance at any time. You can't afford to put off purchase until next year because prices are sure to rise.

   _____

   _____

3. Edgar's Magic Hair Oil contains a substance derived from the skin of sheep. Will this make your hair grow? Will it stop falling hair? Have you ever seen a bald-headed sheep? Get a bottle at the drugstore nearest you today.

   _____

   _____

4. Miss Norma Jackson is now in her third year of teaching history at Roosevelt High School. She has just received notice from the school board that she will not be granted tenure and will not be rehired for next year. No reasons were given. This is a shameful, highhanded action by the school board. Miss Jackson has taught two of my children, and they tell me that she is one of the best teachers they have had. I have met her several times and have found her alert, interesting, and well informed. It would be a great loss to the school if she were dropped from the teaching staff.

   _____

   _____

5. We hear a lot these days about using less gasoline, oil, and other energy sources, but using less is not going to solve our problems. What we need is other sources of

energy. The purpose of the administration's energy bill is to encourage and promote their development. Some day the oil wells and gas wells will run dry, and cutting back here and there will not prevent it. We need to find new ways to heat our houses and run our cars and trucks. Members of Congress should be urged by the people to vote for the administration bill.

———————————————

———————————————

B. Try again. Find two purposes for the language in each item.
Write them on the lines provided.

1. Once or twice a year it is my pleasure to review a really great book. Such a book is *The Ancient World* by the English historian Janet Parker. It is a long book (780 pages) and it is not inexpensive ($17.50). But it makes most rewarding reading. Don't wait for the paperback edition because there may never be one. Go out and buy the book today.

———————————————

———————————————

2. Benjamin Franklin has been accused with some justice of a good many faults and vices, but for all that, he was an extraordinary man. He was thrifty and industrious. He amassed a moderate fortune before he was 40, but he did not settle back in idle luxury. His restless mind was interested in everything from simplified spelling to musical water glasses, for which Mozart composed a sonata. He devised spectacles and a surgical instrument. He served the colonies in England before the Revolution and the United States in France afterward. He was respected alike by European scholars, political leaders, and scientists.

———————————————

———————————————

3. "Warning: The Surgeon General Has Determined That Cigarette Smoking Is

Dangerous to Your Health." (Notice which must appear on every package of cigarettes and in every cigarette advertisement.)

_____

_____

4. On November 3, 1973, *Mariner 10* rocketed from the earth. Within 18 months it had traveled half a billion miles. In February, 1974, it flew within 3,600 miles of Venus and radioed back the first close-up pictures ever taken of the planet. A year later it sent back clear pictures of a large part of Mercury's surface. This is a great triumph of American science and technology. It should give a real lift to us earth-bound citizens, weighed down as we are with everyday problems of living. We can be genuinely proud of this remarkable feat.

_____

_____

5. Marie Anderson sits alone in her one-room apartment. Her only company is the television set. Sometimes there is heat in the apartment; sometimes there is not. Marie Anderson needs medical attention. Her broken hip has not mended properly. She needs food and she needs money. Help us this holiday season to help others. Give to *Help the Helpless*.

_____

_____

Lesson 20.   Reading Newspaper Headlines

The ability to spot the writer's purpose is especially useful in reading newspaper headlines because headlines can serve several different purposes. A careful reader is always on watch for what the headline writer is trying to do.

The first purpose of a headline is *to inform* the reader by summing up the story it covers. Usually this is done with great skill, but sometimes the whole story cannot be stated in a single phrase or sentence. If there are several angles, the headline writer must select the most important one to write about.

The second job of a headline is *to get the reader to do something*—to buy the paper and read the story. The headline must therefore catch attention and arouse curiosity. Sometimes this can be done by an amusing twist. The writer's purpose then is *to amuse* rather than to give information.

For example, "A Shortage of Hearts" was the headline for a story about a decline in heart-transplant operations which left trained staffs with little to do. "1,000 Watts of Woman Power" headed a story about a new radio station set up and run by women.

Creating a headline involves judgment. The writer has to size up the entire reported situation and judge what is important. The important thing may not be a simple fact, but what the fact shows, what it means, or what it foretells. The purpose of the headline writer, then, may be *to express personal feelings or beliefs*.

But the writer is interested in much more than just personal expression. He or she wants to persuade the reader *to believe something*, to accept a point of view. To express feelings and beliefs and to persuade the reader, the headline writer may use judgment words. Note, for example, the italicized words in these headlines:

Community Fund *Falling Short* of Goal
Extra Aid From Federal Government *Doubtful*

Americans *Unmoved* by New Ties to China
Oil Price Increase to *Hit* Northeast *Hardest*

Headlines, then, may do more than state facts. They may also state the opinion, judgment, or belief of the writer. Alert readers will spot what the writer is doing and make up their own minds as to what the facts mean.

Headlines are written under great time pressure, often only minutes before the presses start to run. Writing headlines under these circumstances requires great skill with language, but sometimes the language does not cooperate, and the headline is confusing. Consider this example:

New Gains Reported in Jobless Benefits

Any regular newspaper reader will know that the statement refers to benefits for persons without jobs. From this headline, the reader might assume that *gains in benefits* means that benefits have been increased. This is not what the headline writer intended. The first sentence of the story said:

> A record high of more than 6.6 million persons were receiving unemployment benefits during the week ended July 19, the Department of Labor announced today.

The space allotted to headlines is usually cramped; there is not room for long words. If the headline runs over to a second or third line, the number of letters in each line must be nearly the same, or the headline will look ragged. Hence, headline writers resort to short words, many of them used in a figurative sense.

Alert newspaper readers develop their own translation of headline words and build a dictionary of them in their memories. Here is a list of terms and meanings that will help you understand newspaper headlines.

Newspaper Headline Terms

aide:	an assistant
to *air*:	make public

to **ban**:	oppose, disapprove, or vote against
to **bar**:	oppose or prevent
to **clash**:	fight or disagree
to **curb**:	limit or halt
to **discount**:	deny importance to
to **grill**:	question, interrogate
to **host**:	entertain
to **ink**:	sign
key (noun):	explanation or solution
key (adjective):	most important
pact:	agreement or contract
panel:	committee
parley:	conference
snag:	delay
solon:	senator
to **vow**:	promise or assure
to **weigh**:	consider

MAKE IT WORK

A. Which of the following headlines express an opinion or judgment of the writer? Write *yes* or *no*. The first one is done for you.

1. Uneasy Peace Prevails in Mideast   <u>*yes*</u>

2. Plan for Convention Hall Jeopardized by Protests   _____

3. Terrorists Hold 50 in U.S. Consulate   _____

4. President Begins European Tour   _____

5. Mayor Upset by Criticism of Policies   _____

6. House Committee Angered by Witness' Silence   _____

7. Governor Makes Good Impression on Voters   _____

8. Enthusiastic Crowd Greets Returning Team _____

9. New Yorker Finds Statue of Hadrian in Israel _____

10. Third Man Arrested in Jewel Robbery _____

B. Write the meaning of each italicized word in the following headlines.

1. *Key aide* to governor resigns _____   _____

2. *Panel* to *grill* airline pilots _____   _____

3. *Solons clash* over budget cuts _____   _____

4. Mayor *vows* to *bar* police strike _____   _____

5. City to *host* governors' *parley* _____   _____

6. U.S. *inks pact* with Mexico _____   _____

7. Governor *weighs curb* on school taxes _____   _____

8. Committee *airs clash* over procedures _____   _____

C. Here is a list of headline terms that are not explained on pages 136-37. How many of them do you understand? Write one or two words for the meaning of each term and compare your answers with the key.

1. upped _____

2. to probe _____

3. hopefuls _____

4. to unveil _____

5. to balk _____

6. to spur _____

7. to axe _____

8. to stage _____

9. a drive _____

10. to tap _____

D. For each headline below, three possible meanings are given. Choose the one that makes the most sense. Place an *x* on the line next to it.

1. Future Weighed by Finch College

    (a) The college is studying the future of our society. _____

    (b) The college is considering whether to expand. _____

    (c) The college is considering what it can do in the future. _____

2. City Hall Protest Staged

    (a) A protest meeting of citizens was held at City Hall. _____

    (b) City Hall is putting on a protest program. _____

    (c) City Hall has made a protest to the State capitol. _____

3. Stock Prices Toboggan

    (a) The prices of stocks are rising. _____

    (b) Stock prices are falling rapidly. _____

    (c) Someone named Stock has asked the price of a toboggan. _____

4. Inroads Reported on Garbage Here

    (a) Paths are being made through the garbage. _____

    (b) New plans for garbage disposal have been reported. _____

    (c) The amount of uncollected garbage is decreasing. _____

5. Curbs on Courts Pressed in India

    (a) India is moving to restrict the courts of justice. _____

    (b) India is putting curbs around tennis courts. _____

    (c) Attempts to restrict courts in India have failed. _____

6. Drive to Aid School in Progress

    (a) There is a move to help the school progress, or improve. _____

139

(b) A drive has been started to aid the school. _____

(c) People are driving to a school that gives aid. _____

7. Blaze Fells 9

(a) A fire destroyed 9 buildings. _____

(b) Nine persons were injured in a fire. _____

(c) Nine persons were killed in a fire. _____

8. President's Press Secretary Spars with Reporters

(a) The secretary and reporters had an argument. _____

(b) The secretary and reporters had a fist fight. _____

(c) The secretary took the side of the reporters. _____

9. Volunteers Spur Drive for Metric System

(a) Volunteers halt a drive for the metric system. _____

(b) Volunteers increase efforts to have the metric system adopted. _____

(c) Volunteers fight to halt the drive for adoption of the metric system. _____

10. County Fears Dip in Census

(a) A census shows that fears among people in the county have declined. _____

(b) The county fears that the census will be less complete than before. _____

(c) The county fears that the census will show a dip in county population. _____

E. Try again. Three possible meanings are given for each headline. Choose the one that makes the most sense. Place an *x* on the line next to it.

1. Application for Subdivision to Get Airing

(a) The application will be cleaned up. _____

(b) A request for permission to create a subdivision will be considered publicly. ____

(c) Request for permission to create a subdivision has been thrown out. ____

2. Clash Expected on Mental Bills

(a) Legislative bills on mental health will be opposed. ____

(b) There will be complaints about costs of mental care. ____

(c) There will be a fight over bills dealing with education. ____

3. Candidates Grilled Again

(a) Candidates for office have been roasted again. ____

(b) Candidates for office have been criticized again. ____

(c) Candidates for office have been questioned again. ____

4. Identity of Ghost Writer Revealed

(a) The writer is really a ghost. ____

(b) The ghost has revealed itself. ____

(c) The name of the real author has been discovered. ____

5. 14,000 Sign On Pilgrimage

(a) 14,000 signed something on a pilgrimage. ____

(b) 14,000 have signed up to go on a pilgrimage. ____

(c) There are 14,000 signs announcing a pilgrimage. ____

Lesson 21.   **Check Your Progress**

In the last five lessons you have met a number of important facts and ideas about language. If you can put them to use, they will greatly increase your reading power. They will not only help you to read the words on the page, but to look right through the words, around them, and behind them to get the meaning. Take a few minutes now to reread the first parts of the lessons. Then check your understanding by doing the items below.

I.   If the italicized words have their usual meanings, write *yes*. If they are idioms, write *no*.

1. We could just barely *get by* the truck.   _____

2. We were *crossed up* by the officer's directions.   _____

3. At the last minute, the plans for the entertainment *fell through*.   _____

4. It was five minutes before we *got to the bottom* of the shaft.   _____

5. You can *get by* with that coat anywhere.   _____

6. Kathy could not come in today, but Eva will *fill in* for her.   _____

7. The investigators still haven't *gotten to the bottom* of this case.   _____

8. You can *get across* the river at Allentown.   _____

9. The players decided to *hold out* for a better contract.   _____

10. Someone should *stand by* the door.   _____

II.   A common expression is italicized in each sentence. Three possible meanings for the expression are given. Find the correct meaning and place an *x* on the line next to it.

142

1. On the first day at work, Alvarez *got off on the wrong foot.*

   (a) made a bad start   _____

   (b) was clumsy and awkward   _____

   (c) stumbled   _____

2. Somebody is going to have to *foot the bill* for this extra service.

   (a) add up the figures   _____

   (b) pay   _____

   (c) kick it away   _____

3. The decision was *cut and dried* before the hearing opened.

   (a) changed   _____

   (b) preserved and put away   _____

   (c) settled   _____

4. The real heir was finally *run to earth* in Wyoming where he was working as a ranch hand.

   (a) captured   _____

   (b) located   _____

   (c) seized   _____

5. The disagreement might have been settled quietly, but now the *fat is in the fire.*

   (a) The fire is getting hotter.   _____

   (b) A mistake has been made that cannot be corrected.   _____

   (c) There will be an explosion.   _____

6. Congress seemed to be *playing fast and loose* with the budget.

   (a) acting recklessly   _____

(b) playing without being tense and nervous ____

(c) working rapidly ____

7. Rita has no real *feel for* classical music.

(a) appreciation of or skill in ____

(b) time to practice ____

(c) sense of balance ____

8. In a short time, Bob's real purpose *came to the fore*.

(a) awakened ____

(b) became clear ____

(c) caught up with him ____

9. They dropped out of the club because they couldn't *keep their end up*.

(a) do their share ____

(b) keep up their enthusiasm ____

(c) find time for it ____

10. They were lucky *to break even* on the deal.

(a) get out of it ____

(b) recover costs ____

(c) make a profit ____

III. Decide which statements are figurative and which are literal. Write **F** for figurative and **L** for literal.

1. Bella tried the new recipe with success. ____

2. The school board likes both candidates. ____

3. The board of directors will meet on Tuesday. ____

4. The mayor's office had no comment on the accusation.   ____

5. The store says it is not responsible for the accident.   ____

6. Tom's remark really broke us up.   ____

7. For two days, Maria was floating on air.   ____

8. It is frightening to be lost in a big city.   ____

9. We have trimmed all the fat out of the budget.   ____

10. A ton of bricks weighs no more than a ton of feathers.   ____

11. The church is asking everyone to make an extra contribution.   ____

12. The buzzer announced that someone had entered the office.   ____

13. The plans for the new road are ready.   ____

14. Our plans were upset by Helen's sudden illness.   ____

15. The doctor gave Ellie several suggestions.   ____

IV.   What is the writer saying? Look for the suggested meaning, the belief or feeling that is not stated. Then answer the questions that follow. Write *true* or *false*.

1. The dentist's office is commonly represented as a chamber of horrors where painful tortures are practiced on helpless patients. This notion has kept many people from going to the dentist in time to save a tooth, and in the end, they have to go anyway to have the tooth extracted. Dentists today have new anesthetics and new ways of operating that either prevent pain or reduce it to a minimum. There is probably no such thing as completely "painless dentistry," but usually the discomfort is momentary, and timely dental work can prevent nights of toothache misery.

   (a) The best way to avoid dental pain is to stay away from the dentist's office.   _____

   (b) Dental work today is completely free of pain because of new anesthetics and ways of operating.   _____

   (c) No one should avoid having dental work done out of fear of the pain it may cause.   _____

2. The motors in modern automobiles are designed to permit speeds of 80 or 90 miles an hour. Having paid for all this power, some owners want to enjoy it. And most drivers on the highway seem always to be in a hurry. They defy the facts of life and death. The records show that high speed is a main cause of highway accidents. During the few months when drivers held their speed to the legal limit of 55 miles per hour, fewer accidents occurred. Most cars will go farther on a gallon of gas at moderate speeds than at high speeds. If a driver *averages* 60 miles an hour on a 50-mile trip, he will arrive only a few minutes earlier than if he had averaged 50 miles an hour. So, what's the hurry?

(a) High-speed driving is not worth the time it gains.　　　＿＿＿＿＿＿＿

(b) Automobile motors should not be built with their present power.　　　＿＿＿＿＿＿＿

(c) Moderate speeds are more economical and less dangerous, even with cars that can move at 80 or 90 miles an hour.　　　＿＿＿＿＿＿＿

(d) Drivers who exceed the 55-mile-per-hour speed limit should be arrested and punished.　　　＿＿＿＿＿＿＿

V. Read the following selections and decide on two purposes of the writer. (Two purposes are given in the key, but you may find more than two.) Write them on the lines provided. Choose from the following possible purposes:

to inform	to express feelings
to arouse feelings	to entertain or amuse
to get someone to do something	to hide or confuse meaning
to get someone to believe something	

1. If you think you are sick, you *are* sick no matter what anyone else says. On the other hand, if you have faith in your doctor, and if he tells you that you are going to feel better, you probably will. The effect of the mind upon the body is real and powerful, and it occurs whether one is aware of it or not.

　　Take the case of Mrs. A, for example. She was unable to get to sleep at night. She lacked energy and was too tired during the day even for the simple things that she used to enjoy doing. Occasional headaches, which were becoming more frequent, prevented her from reading or watching television. The more she thought about her condition, the worse she felt. At length, she went to see her doctor, whom she had known for years. The doctor listened to her complaints and gave her a fairly thorough examination. Then, he said to her, "There is nothing seriously wrong with your physical condition, but I accept the fact that you don't feel well. I am going to give you some pills that should help. I want you to take one after dinner and one a half hour before going to bed tonight. Call me tomorrow and tell me how you feel."

The next morning Mrs. A telephoned to say, "Doctor, I had the first good night's sleep last night in two months. Whatever is in those pills?"

The doctor said, "It's an old formula I have used for years. Just keep on taking them for a week." Turning to his nurse, he said, "It's wonderful what a little baking soda can do."

_____

_____

2. You don't have to vote tomorrow. No one can make you go to the polls, but if you knew how hard people have fought in the past to get you the right to vote, you would not just sit at home. You would not take the attitude of the little old lady who said, "I never vote for Congressmen. It only encourages them." Political rights are like muscles: if you don't use them, they wither and fade away. Take the time tomorrow to exercise your right to vote. How would you like it if someone said, "Your right to vote has been abolished"?

_____

_____

VI. Headline words are given on the left. Meanings are listed on the right. Find the meaning for each headline word and write it on the line next to the word.

Words   *Meanings*

1. to grill   _____   delay

2. a panel   _____   consider

147

3. to probe   _____   oppose or prevent

4. to bar   _____   committee

5. to weigh   _____   examine

6. to eye   _____   investigate

7. to clash   _____   limit or halt

8. to vow   _____   question

9. to curb   _____   fight or disagree

10. a snag   _____   promise or assure

VII.   Which of the following headlines express an opinion or belief of the writer? Write *yes* or *no*.

1. Mayor Hears Tax Protests   _____

2. City Hospitals May Be Closed   _____

3. Fears of Inflation Rising   _____

4. County Board Adopts Budget   _____

5. Jury Picked in Robbery Trial   _____

6. President Goes to Camp David for Weekend   _____

7. President Escapes to Camp David for Needed Rest   _____

8. Lack of Rain Threatens Crops   _____

9. Rainfall Lowest in Years   _____

10. Governor Angered by Lobbies   _____

Lesson 22. What Is the Next Sentence Doing?

The most important thing in reading a paragraph is to see how one sentence is related to the next. The reader must make the connections between sentences to understand what the writer is saying.

Sometimes a paragraph may seem to be just a string of unrelated sentences that occurred to the writer as he went along. Usually this is not the case; there are connections even though the writer does not state outright what they are.

Hunting for these connections requires rereading. It may seem a waste of time to go back over a paragraph, but it is not. It may seem to you that rereading is a confession of weakness, but it is not. People in business reread an entire letter to make sure they understand it. Scholars, lawyers, and professional people may go over a paragraph a dozen times to make sure of its meaning.

The surest way for a writer to tie one sentence to another is to use connecting words. You will find it useful to review the connectors in Lesson 7 and to look again at the relations they show: *contrast*, *cause-effect*, and *time*.

The words *it*, *this*, *these*, *that*, and *those* at the beginning of a sentence clearly indicate that the writer is continuing to talk about the same thing:

> *It* is also attractive in appearance.
> *That* was what the voters wanted to know.
> *These* instructions are to be followed exactly.

It is not always used to stand for something already mentioned. Sometimes *it* is used as a sentence starter without referring to what has gone before:

> *It* is likely to snow before evening.
> *It* is true that we were unprepared for what happened.
> *It* appears that I was misunderstood.

Look at the third paragraph of this lesson on page 149. *It* appears five times. Can you spot the two instances in which *it* is a sentence starter?

The first sentence in a paragraph usually gives the reader a fresh, clean start. It often expresses the main idea of the paragraph. The sentences that follow the first one may be used in six different ways:

1. To give *examples*
2. To *explain* by defining, restating, or showing cause or effect
3. To *add a new fact or idea*
4. To show *time order* in which events occurred
5. To give *details*
6. To *summarize* or make a general statement

We will deal with the first three of these uses in this lesson and with the others in the next lesson. The following paragraphs illustrate the first three uses.

1. Example.   The example sentence is easy to spot. If you can insert the words "for example" at the beginning, you know that you have an example sentence.

> Many hitters go through a series of preparatory rituals before stepping into the batter's box. (for example) These include tugging at their caps, touching their uniform letters or medallions, crossing themselves, tapping or bouncing the bat on the plate...(for example) Rocky Calavito, a colorful home-run hitter active in the 1950's and '60s, used to stretch his arm behind his back and cross himself when he came to the plate. (for example) A player in the Texas Ranger organization draws a triangle in the dirt outside the batter's box with the peak pointing to center field.

2. Explanation.   An explanation sentence is used to explain the meaning of the sentence just before it or of some term in that sentence. Thus, an explanation may give a definition, or it may identify some thing or person. Or it may restate the meaning of the entire sentence. Usually this sort of explanation sentence contains one of the writer's signal words. (See Lesson 6.)

An explanation sentence may also state the cause or the effect of what is stated in the preceding sentence. When this happens, a connector usually appears. (See Lesson 7.)

> A peculiar happening on many deserts is the "ghost rain." That is, rain actually falls from a few clouds over the area but disappears before it reaches the ground. (definition) The reason it disappears is that the raindrops strike a level of very hot air and immediately evaporate. (cause)

> During World War II, I was asked to investigate the reasons for the slow recovery of American soldiers suffering from schistosomiasis. This is a parasitic worm infection acquired by bathing in polluted streams. (definition) Many of the GI's who had been struck down by this disease remained in the hospital long after signs of the disease had disappeared. (explains "slow recovery")

3. Adding New Fact or Idea. The regular way of telling something is to go right on from one statement to the next. Each following sentence adds a new fact or idea to what has already been said. The new statement is different in content. It is something *added* to what has gone before. By contrast, an explanation sentence interrupts the flow of thought.

> The custom of celebrating Washington's birthday began informally in 1783 but soon became general. No state legislature set the date as a holiday. (added fact) In 1789 the Congress even refused to pass a resolution congratulating the President on his birthday. (added fact)

Note: In your reading, you will find paragraphs in which the separate sentences are used in all three ways. Your task is to sort them out.

TRY THESE

A. Each sentence after the first is numbered. Decide how it is used. Write *example*, *explanation*, or *added* on the lines below.

1. Substances that exist in one state of matter will under certain conditions change into another state. (1) Thus, ice can be melted and water can be frozen. (2) Dry ice changes to a gas when it is heated. (3) Rubbing alcohol and nail polish also change to a gas and evaporate from opened bottles.

    (1) _____   (2) _____   (3) _____

2. The first ten Amendments to the Constitution are called the Bill of Rights. (1) These amendments protect U.S. citizens from possible abuse of power by the Congress. (2) They were ratified by the states in 1791 without opposition since people believed that the original Constitution did not protect them adequately.

    (1) _____   (2) _____

3. The metric system is a simple set of standards used in measuring. (1) Thus, the meter is the standard unit of length and is divided into 100 centimeters. (2) A centimeter is not quite half an inch. (3) There is also a standard unit for measuring weight, the kilogram. (4) It is equal to about 2.2 pounds.

    (1) _____   (2) _____   (3) _____   (4) _____

4. The science of biology makes use of the basic facts of other sciences. (1) To explain what happens in a single human cell, biologists draw upon chemistry. (2) To explain why deserts occur on the east side of the Rockies, biologists draw upon the physics of air expansion and air flow. (3) Since about one fifth of the earth's surface is composed of deserts, biologists are concerned with how they are formed.

    (1) _____   (2) _____   (3) _____

5. Every cell in the human body is bathed in lymph. (1) Actually, lymph is the fluid part of the blood and is a clear, watery substance. (2) Lymph is the fluid that fills

up a blister. (3) Lymph is carried through the body in its own system of vessels, comparable to veins and arteries that circulate full blood.

(1) ——————— (2) ——————— (3) ———————

B. Try again. Write *example*, *explanation*, or *added* for each of the numbered sentences.

1. Consumer debt has risen at the rate of 9% a year for the past 20 years. (1) Consumer debt is the amount owed by individuals to stores, dealers, banks, etc. for the purchase of goods and services. (2) A young married couple needing furniture, a house, or a car may make a partial payment in cash and agree to pay the balance in installments. (3) One reason for the rise in consumer debt is the increase in the number of marriages.

(1) ——————— (2) ——————— (3) ———————

2. Some of the birds found in the Sahara Desert have developed remarkable ways of avoiding predators. (1) A predator is an animal that hunts and kills other animals for its food. (2) One of the most remarkable of the Sahara birds is the spotted sand grouse, whose worst enemy is the falcon. (3) The spotted sand grouse preserves its safety through its coloring, which is identical with that of the rocks among which it sits motionless for hours. (4) The sand grouse is also remarkable for its ability to carry water under its wings for miles from a water hole to its nest.

(1) ——————— (2) ——————— (3) ——————— (4) ———————

3. Because of its salt content, only a few organisms inhabit the water of Great Salt Lake. (1) A few species of bacteria and salt-resistant algae live there, manufacturing their own food by photosynthesis. (2) These algae provide food for the only animal that lives in the water, the brine shrimp. (3) In some seasons the algae multiply so rapidly that they color the water of the lake orange, green, or red, depending upon the species.

(1) ——————— (2) ——————— (3) ———————

Lesson 23.   More About the Next Sentence

Time Order.   You will recall from Lesson 7 that connectors are used to show three ways of looking at time, which were identified as *earlier*, *during*, and *later*. The connectors are used not only within sentences but *between* sentences to tie one statement to the next.

Time order is essential in any narrative. It is also important in the explanation of any process from the start to the finish. It is often indicated by connectors such as *earlier*, *meanwhile*, *after*, *then*, etc. But in some narrative accounts, these words do not appear, and the reader must assume that events occurred in the order in which they are reported.

Not all the sentences in a narrative account are used to express time order. Occasionally, the writer must halt his story to explain or to give an example. Note the italicized sentence in the paragraph below.

> At the close of the last Ice Age, the northern part of Africa turned green. People and animals began to move into an area that had once been desert. At one point they halted near a cluster of tall, thin columns of red sandstone. *These columns give the appearance of fingers of some huge buried hand.* (explanation) Then an unknown artist picked up a piece of rock and drew a remarkable picture on one of the columns.

Details.   Details are a necessary part of any explanation or description. In the next lesson you will learn that details are also a necessary part of a news story.

You may wonder what is the difference between a detail and an example. A detail is a *part* of the thing, event, or situation being presented. An example is only an instance of how a general idea or principle works. You can always insert the words *for instance* or *for example* before an example. You cannot do this with a detail. Try inserting these words before the two sentences marked "detail" below.

154

Shortly before the pilot and his plane disappeared without a trace in Australian waters, he radioed, "I am being followed by a huge object. *It is greenish in color and has three lights.* (detail) *Its shape is round.*" (detail)

Summary or General Statement. In most kinds of reading, a summary or general statement may come at the start of the paragraph, at the end, or even in the middle. The summary sentence ties all the others together. It is the sentence to which all the others relate.

In the summer of 1793, some of the citizens of Baltimore complained of a rapid pulse, a hot skin, rough tongue, inflamed eyes, and dull pains in the head and loins. Toward the close of the fourth day, the whites of the eyes turned yellow, there was bleeding from the nose, and the body turned a yellowish purple color. And on about the eighth day the victims would die. *This was the yellow fever.* (summary) Within three weeks there was scarcely a family in the city without one or more patients. The mayor ordered the walks and streets to be cleaned. Doctors, at their wits' end, prescribed any treatment suggested to them, from burning fires, burning gunpowder, to chewing garlic or tobacco.

SEE FOR YOURSELF

A. Find the sentence in each paragraph that is *not* used to show time order. Underline it. Decide how it is used. Write *detail*, *example*, or *explanation* on the line provided.

1. Midway in World War II, Churchill was faced with a terrifying decision. British Intelligence had broken the radio code used by the German air force, and for more than a year, the British knew when and where air raids would come. Suddenly, they learned of a plan to bomb Coventry. This was to be a massive raid which would obliterate the town, but if people were moved out in advance, the Germans would know that their code had been broken. After much thought and consultation, Churchill decided to sacrifice Coventry and retain control of the code. Coventry was destroyed.

_____

2. A Russian fishing trawler has picked up four American flyers from icy Alaskan waters, into which they fell when the electric system of their plane failed. All four flyers survived the mishap. They are now on their way back to this country.

_____

3. In the fall, the monarch butterfly begins its annual flight south from its summer feeding grounds. The monarch is distinguished by its reddish-brown wings that are edged with black. It moves through a notch in the Green Mountains and keeps a steady pace toward its winter quarters. Some weeks later it arrives in the Southwest, having made a flight of nearly 3,000 miles.

_____

B. Decide what use the italicized sentence serves in each paragraph below. Write *example*, *detail*, or *summary*.

1. When the first settlers arrived on the Atlantic coast, they fought the forests to make room for crops and houses. Later, pioneers hacked their way through the dense tree growths to make trails for their wagons. *For 200 years or more, the forests were regarded by westward-moving Americans as an enemy to be uprooted and destroyed.* Space was needed for railroad tracks, roads, settlements, and farms, and the forests had to give way.

_____

2. When Jefferson became President in 1801, travel in this country was difficult and uncomfortable. Accommodations at inns along the way or even in New York City were not "rough and ready"; they were simply rough. *The traveler slept in the first bed he found empty, or, if all were occupied, lay down on one beside its occupant without the courtesy of asking leave.* If he asked for clean sheets, he was thought to be unreasonable, since sheets were changed infrequently and only at stated times.

_____

3. The huge open space before St. Peter's in Rome is called St. Peter's Square, but it is not a square at all. It is an ellipse, not quite a circle, since it is 240 meters in width and 200 in length. *The sides are enclosed by a circular covered walk which is lined by 284 columns in four rows.* The spectacular design of the "Square" is the work of Giovani Bernini, the great architect, sculptor, and painter.

_____

C. Each sentence in the following paragraph is numbered. Decide how each sentence is used. Write *summary, detail, example,* or *time* on the lines provided.

(1) After many travels and years of neglect, the original copy of the *Declaration of Independence* has been safely lodged in the National Archives Building in Washington, D.C. (2) It followed the Continental Congress during the Revolutionary War as the Congress moved from place to place seeking safety. (3) It was later handed to Washington when he was inaugurated in New York. (4) The document was always respected but sometimes neglected and badly cared for. (5) During the years it hung in the Patent Office, it was exposed to sunlight, so the ink faded. (6) Today, it is protected by insulating glass and a cellulose backing, and at nightfall it is lowered by machinery into a lead-lined vault where it is safe from any radiation.

(1) _____   (3) _____   (5) _____

(2) _____   (4) _____   (6) _____

Lesson 24. Reading the News Story

Today's newspapers are primarily concerned with reporting the news, but they also carry the opinions of the newspaper's owners, editors, and columnists. The newspaper ideal is to keep fact and opinion separate by labeling opinion as "editorial." Needless to say, this ideal is not always honored in practice, and some papers have a frank bias for or against political parties, persons, and ideas.

While the prime concern of modern newspapers is the news, they also provide services and information in wide variety. In many papers, current news occupies considerably less space than articles on decorating, gardening, home repairs, cooking, and other subjects. These articles are written by people who are experts or hard-working students of their fields.

The news stories are the work of other experts, reporters who are trained to dig out the facts. These men and women are devoted to finding out not only *what* happened, but *why* and *how* it happened. They type or dictate their findings in "stories," which go to editors and rewrite specialists for checking and revision.

The first paragraph of the news story—called the **lead**—states the essential facts: *what* happened, *where* and *when* it happened, and *who* was involved. Formerly, all this was crowded into one long complicated sentence. Today, the growing practice is to state what happened in the first sentence and to place the other information in following sentences.

Succeeding paragraphs provide additional information to explain, if possible, *how* and *why* something happened. The paragraphs decline in importance as they near the end. The reason for this arrangement is that lack of space may force the editors to cut the story.

The newspaper ideal is to state only facts in the lead paragraph. The opinion, judgment, or interpretation of the reporter is not considered to be a reportable fact. The opinions of others, however—eyewitnesses, observers, government officials— are news and are reportable facts. Sometimes, nonetheless, the judgment of the reporter creeps in. Compare

The President sent his budget for the forthcoming fiscal year
to Congress today.

The President sent his budget for the forthcoming fiscal year
to Congress today, and *it is already in trouble.*

In many situations, facts are not uncovered all at once. They
emerge from time to time, and they are recorded in "continuation"
stories. Since there is seldom space for a complete review of earlier
information, the reader may not be aware of the significance of
the later stories. In the fall of 1978, newspapers reported "Airline
crash kills 140." Later stories on the same day reported "Private
plane cause of airline crash." On the next day, it was reported that
"Second private plane was involved in air disaster." A week later,
the story was "Second plane theory discounted." In short, keeping
up with the news involves remembering what was reported before.

TRY IT OUT

A. The sentences in the news story below are numbered. Read
the story and then answer the questions that follow.

(1) The government's war on cancer is "a medical Vietnam" according to Donald
Kennedy, the U.S. Food and Drug Commissioner.
(2) "Vast amounts of money and effort are pumped into battle," he said today, "yet
victory seems no closer."
(3) Seven years have passed and $5 billion have been spent since the President and
the Congress began an all-out drive to find a cure.
(4) Some legislators spoke of solving the cancer problem before the country's 200th
birthday in 1976.
(5) Today, though, a cancer cure is still just a hope.
(6) Indeed, some researchers say the more they learn about cancer, the less likely a
single cure seems.

Write the number of the sentence in which you find the answer
to each question.

1. Which sentence expresses the writer's opinion? _____

2. In which sentence is the Food and Drug Commissioner quoted? _____

3. Which sentence quotes those who believe that a single cure for cancer is unlikely? _____

4. Which sentence tells who believed that the cancer problem would be solved by 1976? _____

5. Which sentence gives the detail to support the Commissioner's opinion? _____

B. Read the news story below and then answer the questions that follow.

The rumors are apparently fact: Bobby Fischer, former world chess champion, will return to competition after six years' retirement, a Yugoslavian chess official states. Miles Milanovich, president of the Serbian Chess Federation, said yesterday that Fischer is in Yugoslavia to arrange a match with grandmaster Svetozar Gligoric in 1979. Fischer is seeking a $1 million fee, Gligoric said. Chess fans here reported last week that Fischer was interested in playing the grandmaster. Fischer did not confirm these reports.

1. Whose opinion is it that the rumors are fact?

_____

2. Who said that Fischer was in Yugoslavia to arrange a match?

_____

3. Who reported that Fischer was interested in playing Gligoric?

_____

4. Did Fischer agree that this is the case?

_____

5. Who said that Fischer wants a $1 million fee?

_____

C. Read the paragraphs and then answer the questions that follow.

(1) The American spacecraft _Venus 2_ was launched yesterday from Kennedy Space Center. It is expected to complete the 220 million mile journey in four months, arriving at its destination December 9.

(2) The probe of Earth's closest planetary neighbor is designed to provide detailed information on the nature of the atmosphere of Venus. Sensing instruments will record information on the composition, circulation, and energy balance of the atmosphere that have been lacking heretofore.

(3) Spacecraft engineers have been faced with severe problems in designing a craft to withstand the intense heat and pressure known to exist in the Venetian atmosphere. The instrument viewing ports on one of the Pioneer Venus probes had to be made of sapphire and a 13.5 carat diamond the size of a quarter. Diamond is the only material transparent to infrared light and still able to withstand tremendous heat and pressure.

1. Which paragraph tells _what_ happened? _____

2. Which paragraph gives detail as to _how_ the spacecraft was designed? _____

3. Which paragraph tells _why_ the spacecraft was launched? _____

D. Read the paragraphs and then answer the questions that follow.

(1) A bus carrying 41 mentally and physically handicapped people went out of control on a hill last night, left the highway, and plunged into Lake D'Argent, 50 miles east of Montreal. All 41 of the passengers were drowned, but the driver and six volunteer assistants escaped before the bus sank into 60 feet of water.

(2) A survivor said the brakes had failed and the driver had been unable to make a turn at the bottom of the hill.

161

(3) "The bus started to speed, and the driver told me to tell everyone to get set because he was going to do a 90-degree turn," the survivor said. "But at the speed we were going, he couldn't turn and we dove right into the water."

(4) "I managed to get the door open, saw a boat and swam for it. But I couldn't get it free from its mooring. Neighbors tried to help, but we couldn't get it loose."

(5) The bus stayed afloat for about five minutes before sinking. Apparently none of the passengers was physically able to escape.

1. Which paragraph tells *what* happened? _____

2. Which paragraphs tell *how* it happened? _____

3. Which paragraphs tell *why* the loss of life was so great? _____

E. The following paragraphs are the first paragraphs of newspaper stories. Which of the paragraphs state the opinion of the writer and which quote the opinion of other persons? Write *writer* or *others*.

1. A barge oil spill threatens to close beaches in a tourist area of Puerto Rico, a Coast Guard spokesman said today. _____

2. The Interior Department today substantially modified its rules on the protection of nearly 50 million acres of Alaskan land. _____

3. Up to 40 percent of this year's citrus fruit crop may have been damaged by the hard freeze that gripped California last month. _____

4. Prices that farmers get for raw products rose 3 percent in December, the Agriculture Department said today. _____

5. There will be a serious epidemic of flu this winter, U.S. medical authorities stated today. _____

6. The Yankee baseball team was met at the Newark airport last night by a boisterous and unruly crowd of fans. _____

7. Brush fires fanned by desert winds raged out of control last night near Los Angeles. _____

8. There is a 95 percent probability that a second gunman fired at John F. Kennedy when the former President was assassinated in Dallas in 1963, acoustics experts said today. _____

Lesson 25. **Watch the Details**

In a news story you get a general idea of what happened from the headline or the first sentence of the story itself. This may be all you want to know or all you need to know, but if you want to talk about the incident, the general idea is not enough. You need specific items to back it up and give it meaning. You need *details*.

The details are the small parts that make up the whole of a situation, or of a story about a situation. The details are the items that explain or give meaning to a general statement. Usually, in your reading you must give attention to details and remember them.

Suppose, for example, that you want to know whether you must file an income tax return. A *return* is a statement made by writing information on a form provided by the Internal Revenue Service (IRS). The return is *filed* by mailing or delivering it to an IRS office. Many people who file returns do not have to pay any income tax. The question is whether you are required to *file* a return.

To find out, you get a copy of instructions issued by the IRS. The instructions state: "A citizen or resident of the United States, or a resident of Puerto Rico, must file a federal income tax return if he or she falls within any of the following categories and meets the filing requirements of that category." A *category* is a class of things or persons that are of the same kind.

This is a general statement. To answer your question, you need to know 1) what class or category you belong to and 2) whether your category must file a return. The answers to these questions are provided in the details of the instructions.

Details are important whenever you are looking for information. They are important in understanding the meaning of general statements that you meet in any of your reading in newspapers, textbooks, or instruction manuals.

IT'S YOUR TURN

A. Read the following news story and answer the questions that follow. Write *yes* or *no* on the line next to the question.

State governments did better financially than the federal government in fiscal 1977, piling up a $13.3 billion surplus. By comparison the federal government had a deficit close to $50 billion for the year. These figures were released in a report from the Census Bureau, published yesterday.

Total expenditures for state governments reached $191.2 billion, an increase of 5.1 percent over the previous year. The increases fell in the areas of education, welfare, highways, and support of hospitals, in that order.

Expenditures were more than offset by increased revenues. Taxes provided $101.1 billion, nearly 60 percent of the revenue, with an increase of 19 percent in income taxes alone. Sales taxes provided nearly $60 billion. State lotteries in 13 states contributed nearly $1.2 billion during the fiscal year.

1. State governments improved their financial condition by reducing expenditures. _____

2. Welfare costs accounted for the largest share of the costs of state governments. _____

3. Part of the increase in state revenues came from higher income taxes. _____

4. The federal government deficit was close to $13.3 billion. _____

5. State lotteries were a source of revenue in some states. _____

B. Read the following paragraphs and answer the questions that follow. Write *yes* or *no*.

When a corporation wishes to expand significantly, it often sells *stock*, or shares of ownership. Purchasers of stock become owners of the business, although actual title to specific assets is retained by the corporation. The corporation will never refund money invested by stockholders, although investors can sell their stock to other investors if they wish.

Shareholders, being part owners of the business, are entitled to share in the corporation's profits. Such profits are distributed as *dividends*, usually quarterly. However, since a company may not be profitable in a certain year, or may wish to plow back some or all of its earnings into the business, dividends are not always declared. People who buy shares of stock do so for one of three principal reasons: (1) they hope to earn dividends, (2) they believe the stock will increase in price over a period of months or years, or (3) they are speculating—that is, hoping for a rapid increase in the price of the stock in a short period of time.

1. A person who buys stock is assured of receiving dividends every year. _____

2. A stockholder is a part owner of the business whose stock he owns. _____

3. As part owner, the stockholder owns part of the buildings, the trucks, the merchandise, and other assets of the company. _____

4. If a stockholder becomes dissatisfied with his investment, he can sell the stock back to the company. _____

5. Some people who buy stocks are less interested in dividends than in the possible increase in the price of the stock, which they would then sell at a profit. _____

C. Read the paragraphs below and then answer the questions that follow. Write *yes* or *no*.

Milk inspection and grading are based on U.S. government standards in use throughout the country. Milk grades range from "Certified" through "Grade A," "Grade B," and "Grade C." The lower the grade, the more bacteria are permitted in a given quantity of milk. These bacteria are not harmful to human beings but indicate under what conditions and for what length of time the milk has been stored.

Milk prices depend upon the amount of butterfat in the milk. Compared to whole milk, which contains 5% butterfat, skimmed milk containing only 2% butterfat may cost 5 cents less per quart. Dried milks are graded by taste appeal. They are low in fat but otherwise are comparable in nutritional value to whole milk.

1. The highest grade of milk is labeled "Certified." _____

2. Milk that is labeled "Grade C" contains bacteria that are harmful to human beings. _____

3. Skimmed milk contains more butterfat than whole milk and therefore costs more. _____

4. Dried milks are graded on the basis of how much butterfat they contain. _____

5. Except for fat content, dried milks have just as much nutritional value as whole milk. _____

Lesson 26. Practical Reading

In practical reading your purpose is to find out how to do something. You want detailed information that will help you do it. The printed materials that you consult for this purpose do not deal with general ideas. They provide only detailed information. Your problems as a reader are 1) to locate the information and 2) to get the details straight.

Directories. Directories and catalogues exist for many purposes. Libraries have catalogues of the books in their collections. In almost every kind of business, there are catalogues which list suppliers of items used in that business. In a large building there is usually a directory in the lobby to show the location of offices—the floor number and the office number on that floor.

The most frequently used directory is the telephone directory. It lists the telephone number and the address of the subscribers, the people who have telephones. The "Yellow Pages" contains a listing of firms that supply products and services.

All these directories are arranged alphabetically so that if you know how a name is spelled, you can find it easily. But there are some special problems. Most telephone directories provide guides in their front pages for finding names and numbers, for example:

1. The last name appears first. Initials, first names, and titles follow: Blake, J.L. Dr. (This is Dr. J.L. Blake.)
2. Some abbreviations appear as if they were spelled out: St. John's is listed alphabetically as though "St." were spelled out: *Saint* John's. Mt. Horeb is listed alphabetically as though spelled *Mount*.
3. Government offices are listed under the name of the town, city, or state. Federal government offices are listed under *United States*.
4. Names with prefixes are generally treated as one word. Thus *DiFabbio* follows *Diez*. *McKay* follows *Mack*. *McAdam* follows *Mazzurco* because *Mc* alphabetically follows *Ma*.

Keep in mind that there are different ways of spelling a name. If you were looking up the number of someone whose name is pronounced *Shoo•man*, you might have to try *Schuman*, *Schumann*, *Shuman*, or *Shumann*. Similarly, in using the "Yellow Pages," you may be directed to look under another heading. For example, if you wanted someone to repair a garage door, you would find under the heading "Garage Doors" the instruction to look under "Doors."

Transportation Schedules. Every airline, bus company, or railroad is required to publish a schedule showing departure times at every stop—except in some city transit systems. If no time is shown for a station, the train, bus, or airplane does not make that stop. Express transports which go directly between cities are usually indicated by a heavy black line between the names of the cities.

The lightface figures on a schedule indicate A.M. departure and arrival times, and A.M. starts at midnight. Boldface figures indicate P.M. times, and P.M. starts at noon. Since fewer transports operate on weekends and holidays, schedules usually list departure and arrival times for these days in a separate section. On most schedules, you will find small letters next to the station stop or the number of the bus, train, or airplane. The meaning of these letters is shown in one place on the schedule; for example, they may indicate "Sundays only," "Daily except Saturday, Sunday, and Holidays," "Meal served," or "Rest stop."

Recipes and Instructions. In following a recipe, you want to know the quantities to be used, the order in which to put them together, and usually how long to cook the dish and at what temperature. Quantities are stated in standard measurements: a cup of flour is not a teacup but a standard measuring cup of flour.

For most appliances, the manufacturer supplies a set of directions for their care and use. For toys and other articles that the customer must assemble, directions usually have a diagram that names and identifies the parts. Here again, the order in which things are to be done is important.

DO IT YOURSELF

A. Look over the following example from a telephone directory and answer the questions that follow.

Finch, Alice   160 E. 71 743-0292
Finch, Alan B. Rev.   1421 W. Lake 765-8260
Finch, Allen C.   24 Drew Pl 765-7165
Finch, Alvin C. Dr.   142 3 Av.................... 551-0291
Finch, A.J.   1401 Park St.................................. 679-0881
Finch, Andrew lwr   270 Grand Ave 679-6278
　　　　　　res   692 Pleasant Dr.................. 753-4290
Finch, Charles M. dentist   146 Broadway 688-0533
Finch, Charles M. Jr.   1748 Central Ave........ 243-8824

1. What is the address of the Finch who is a pastor?   _____

2. What is the home telephone number of the Finch who is a lawyer?   _____

3. What is the telephone number of Allen C. Finch?   _____

4. What is the address of the Finch who is a dentist?   _____

5. What is the telephone number of the dentist's son?   _____

6. What is the address of Doctor Finch?   _____

B. Answer the following questions.

1. What would you find the local FBI number listed under?   _____

2. Is M. McVey listed before or after M. Macbride?   _____

3. Is Mt. Morris listed before or after Morris and Company?   _____

169

4. Is St. Ann's Church listed before or after Singer Publications?   _____

C. Here is part of a bus schedule for service between Pittsburgh and Philadelphia. Look over the schedule carefully and then read the statements below. Write *yes* or *no*.

		F Sun	*E Sun*	*Sun*	
Pittsburgh, PA Lv.	8 45		12 01	2 30	6 30
Carlisle			4 10	6 40	
Harrisburg		3 10	4 45	7 55	11 15
Allentown			6 45	9 55	
Philadelphia	3 40	5 30	7 45	11 00	1 40

F Sun—Friday and Sunday only
E Sun—Except Sunday
Sun—Sunday only

1. There is only one nonstop bus from Pittsburgh to Philadelphia.   _____

2. If you want to go from Pittsburgh to Carlisle on Friday, there is only one bus to take.   _____

3. Only one bus from Pittsburgh stops at Allentown on weekdays.   _____

4. You cannot get from Harrisburg to Allentown on weekdays.   _____

5. You can get a bus from Harrisburg to Philadelphia at 3:10 P.M. every day of the week.   _____

6. You can leave Carlisle for Allentown every day of the week.   _____

7. You can leave Pittsburgh on the 6:30 P.M. bus and arrive in Allentown shortly after midnight.   _____

8. You can leave Pittsburgh at 6:30 A.M. and arrive in Philadelphia early in the afternoon.   _____

D. Read the following recipe carefully. Then read the statements that follow and mark them *yes* or *no*.

Eggplant Casserole

1 medium-sized eggplant
1 small onion
½ 10-oz can condensed mushroom soup
½ cup grated Swiss cheese

2 tablespoons tomato paste
2 teaspoons salt
1 tablespoon cooking oil

Procedure

Turn on oven and set it at 350°. Assemble the utensils you will need including a 2-quart casserole or baking dish.

Peel eggplant and cut it into ½-inch cubes. Place cubes in a colander or strainer and steam until eggplant is soft. Do not let it get mushy.

Chop onion fine and fry in cooking oil over slow heat until it is soft, stirring constantly (about 4 minutes). Remove from heat, add the eggplant and 1 teaspoon salt.

Place the eggplant-onion mixture in casserole. Add 1 teaspoon salt, mushroom soup, tomato paste, and cheese, but keep out 1 tablespoon cheese. Stir mixture gently to distribute the ingredients evenly.

Sprinkle remaining cheese over the top. Place casserole in oven and bake until bubbles rise at the sides (about 20 minutes).

1. The recipe calls for 2 tablespoons of salt. _____

2. The eggplant is salted before it is steamed. _____

3. The tomato paste is added to the onions while they are frying. _____

4. The first thing to do after turning on the oven is to peel the eggplant. _____

5. The mushroom soup is diluted with milk before it is added to the mixture. _____

Final Test

I. Three meanings are given for the italicized word in each pair of sentences. Decide which meaning fits each sentence. Write the number of this meaning on the line provided.

Example: a. Under Dr. Cargill's *dispensation*, the hospital provided better service at less cost.   _____3_____

        b. The mayor stopped the *dispensation* of favors to political friends.   _____1_____

        (1) distribution
        (2) release from an obligation
        (3) management

1. a. We could *discern* no difference between the two bids.   _____

   b. Bob's reasons for leaving were hard to *discern*.   _____

     (1) distinguish
     (2) recognize
     (3) figure out

2. a. The company will spend $1 million to *promote* the new product.   _____

   b. The meetings will *promote* an understanding of the school programs among parents and taxpayers.   _____

     (1) advance to a higher position
     (2) publicize and advertise
     (3) increase or develop

3. a. It was hard to *sustain* an interest in ancient history during the excitement and hardships of wartime.   _____

   b. Home owners *sustain* severe damages to their property from brush fires every year.   _____

(1) keep up
(2) suffer
(3) encourage

4. a. The summer home on the coast *affords* the President privacy and relaxation.   _____

b. He can't *afford* to speak frankly.   _____

(1) has enough money for
(2) is able to act without risk
(3) furnishes

5. a. Jane sat slumped over in an *attitude* of despair.   _____

b. The mechanic's *attitude* toward customers was always disrespectful.   _____

(1) opinion
(2) manner of acting
(3) body position which shows feelings

II. Read each paragraph to find the meaning of the italicized word. Decide which of the possible meanings below the paragraph fits the word. Place an *x* on the line next to it.

1. Scientists from fields as different as physiology and oceanography have reasons for studying sound and its effects upon people. To do this they sometimes construct an *anechoic* chamber. Every square inch of the room—floor, walls, and ceiling—is covered with rugs or heavy pads. In such a room you cannot hear a proverbial pin drop; you couldn't hear a siren wail. No noise from the outside can be heard. If there were any noise on the inside you could not hear it. There are no echoes because all sound is absorbed by the rugs and hangings.

Anechoic means
(a) heavily padded   _____

(b) quiet   _____

(c) free from sound or echo   _____

2. Charles Goodyear discovered the secret of making rubber when a few drops of a mixture he was working with fell on a hot stove. Alexander Fleming discovered the effects of penicillin when he happened to take a second look at a glass slide he was about to throw away. Modern technology owes much to such instances of *serendipity*. The term comes from the title of a fairy tale "The Three Princes of Serendip," in which the princes made happy discoveries in a similar manner.

Serendipity means
(a) making discoveries through experiments   _____

(b) making discoveries through chance or accident   _____

(c) making discoveries by taking a second look   _____

3. It was once thought that the earth's crust is continuous, existing in one unbroken sheet of rock. Recent studies of the structure of the crust seem to show that it is composed of a number of gigantic plates which are in constant motion. The continents (the land surfaces) ride securely attached to the plates. These studies, known as *techtonics*, show that the coast of California is gradually pushing northward and that the Indian subcontinent is pushing up against southern Asia, thus forcing the Himalaya mountains higher and higher. Research on how the earth's surface is put together has led scientists to believe that all the continents were at one time a single mass.

Techtonics deals with
(a) the structure of the earth's crust   _____

(b) the techniques by which plates in the earth's surface were made   _____

(c) prediction of earthquakes   _____

III.   Decide what meaning the prefix or combining form adds to each word below. Write the meaning on the line provided. If the beginning letters are not a prefix, write *none*.

1. biometrics   _____   **4.** autograph   _____

2. minibus   _____   **5.** malformed   _____

3. extrasensory   _____   **6.** mallet   _____

7. hypertension _____   14. union _____

8. intrastate _____   15. unload _____

9. televise _____   16. realize _____

10. monosyllable _____   17. income _____

11. export _____   18. irresponsible _____

12. example _____   19. semicircle _____

13. reappear _____   20. misplaced _____

IV. By dropping the prefixes and suffixes, find the base word in each word below. Be alert for changes in spelling made when suffixes were added. Write the base word.

1. impressionist _____   11. degradation _____

2. insensitive _____   12. deactivation _____

3. subdivision _____   13. unenforceable _____

4. accompanying _____   14. eventuality _____

5. accountability _____   15. interplanetary _____

6. affirmation _____   16. immeasurably _____

7. devaluation _____   17. personification _____

8. concentric _____   18. irregularity _____

9. discontinuous _____   19. unalterably _____

10. dislocation _____   20. correlation _____

V. Which of the following statements are figurative? Which are literal? Write *F* for figurative and *L* for literal.

1. The bank says it can't trace the check. _____

2. These glasses do not help me. _____

3. She won the election by a landslide. _____

4. Her record is an open book. _____

5. The doctor's face told us a great deal. _____

6. Down the road, red lights were flashing. _____

7. The management has asked me to make an announcement. _____

8. The answer was clear to everyone. _____

9. Silence is golden. _____

10. The company has decided not to move. _____

VI. Read each paragraph and answer the questions that follow it. Write *yes* or *no*.

1. The U.S. Oil Corporation announced today that Peter J. Rodino has resigned as president of the company. Mr. Don Jones, chairman of the board, will assume the duties of chief executive officer, a post he held prior to Mr. Rodino's election to the presidency two years ago. Mr. Rodino told a *News* reporter today that he had resigned for personal reasons. Mr. Jones could not be reached either at his home or his office for comment. Mr. Rodino's resignation follows two years of declining sales and profits.

   a. The writer states that Mr. Rodino was fired. _____

   b. Mr. Jones confirmed that Mr. Rodino was fired. _____

   c. Mr. Rodino was the chief executive officer at the time he resigned. _____

   d. Mr. Jones had no previous experience in managing the company. _____

   e. The writer suggests that Mr. Rodino was fired because of declining sales and profits. _____

2. Over the country as a whole, hospital costs have been rising at the rate of more than $1 million per hour, or more than $7 billion per year. Since hospitals are nonprofit organizations, these costs are passed on to the patients. The costs have gone so far out of control that hospitals are trying to "limit" the rate of increase to "only" 12 percent a year. We support a national health insurance program that will give hospitals an incentive to really hold down their costs.

  a. The writer believes that a 12 percent rate of increase in hospital costs is satisfactory. _____

  b. The writer explains how a national health insurance program will provide incentives for hospitals to keep down their costs. _____

  c. The writer believes that hospitals are making an unreasonable profit from their increased charges. _____

  d. The writer's purpose is to arouse feeling against the hospitals. _____

  e. The cost of operating a hospital has been rising at the rate of $1 million per hour. _____

VII. Which of the following headlines express the judgment or the opinion of the writer? Write *yes* or *no*.

1. Nation's politics mired in apathy _____

2. 170 hurt in ferry mishap _____

3. Garbage disposal problems continue to grow _____

4. Desperate Colts look for new quarterback _____

5. U.S. offers aid to China in energy development _____

6. Consumer debt grows in past month _____

7. Voters skeptical as election nears _____

8. Hopes for Mideast peace fade in Washington _____

9. Signing of tax cut delayed by President   _____

10. FBI arrests man in bank theft   _____

VIII. In the following paragraphs, decide how each numbered sentence is being used. Choose from the following possible uses and write your choices on the lines provided.

example	added information
explain	summary

A. At several times in the past, the Mediterranean has been a narrow, fresh-water lake which dried up and later came to life again. (1) The water was fresh, not salty, because it came from melted snow and rains that poured down from the neighboring mountains. (2) When Africa and Europe pulled away from each other, sea water flowed through the gap at the new Straits of Gibraltar, making the Mediterranean an inland sea.

(1) _____   (2) _____

B. Some words have been put together in astonishing ways. (1) The word *behave* is one of them. (2) It means "to act" or "to conduct oneself in a particular way." (3) It is composed of two words, *be* and *have*. (4) It is hard to understand why these two words were joined to produce a word with the meanings and pronunciation of *behave*.

(1) _____   (2) _____   (3) _____   (4) _____

C. The first few Congresses did their best to make life miserable for President Washington. (1) They refused his advice about treaties. (2) They opposed any recognition of his birthday. (3) They would not permit members of his cabinet on the floor of the House or the Senate. (4) All in all, relations between the President and the Congress were not pleasant.

(1) _____   (2) _____   (3) _____   (4) _____

Key

LESSON 1

A.

2. x

B.

1. no
2. yes
3. no
4. yes
5. yes
6. no
7. yes
8. no
9. no
10. no

C.

1. yes
2. no
3. yes
4. yes
5. yes
6. no
7. no
8. yes
9. yes
10. no

D.

1. same
2. same
3. different
4. different
5. different
6. same
7. different
8. same

9. different
10. different

E.

1. a
2. b
3. a
4. b
5. b
6. b
7. b
8. a
9. a
10. b
11. a
12. b
13. a
14. b
15. b
16. a
17. a
18. b
19. b
20. a
21. a
22. a
23. b
24. b
25. a

F.

1. a
2. b
3. c
4. a
5. b
6. d
7. a
8. d
9. c
10. d

LESSON 2

A.

5. x

B.

1. a. 2
   b. 3
   c. 1
   d. 2
   e. 1
2. a. 3
   b. 2
   c. 1
   d. 2
   e. 4
3. a. 1
   b. 2
   c. 1
   d. 3
   e. 4
4. a. 1
   b. 2
   c. 1
   d. 3
   e. 4

C.

1. b
2. b
3. c
4. c
5. c
6. c
7. b
8. c
9. a
10. b

LESSON 3

A.

1. false
2. false
3. true
4. true
5. false
6. true

B.

1. b
2. a
3. a
4. c
5. a
6. b
7. a
8. c
9. c
10. b

C.

1. c
2. b
3. b
4. a
5. c
6. b
7. b
8. c
9. c
10. a

LESSON 4

A.

1. false
2. true
3. true

179

4. false
5. false

B.

1. a
2. a
3. b
4. a
5. b
6. a
7. a
8. b
9. b
10. b

C.

1. c
2. a
3. b
4. b
5. a
6. a
7. c
8. a
9. a
10. a

D.

1. e
2. c
3. b
4. d
5. b
6. c
7. c
8. d
9. d
10. f

LESSON 5

I.

1. true

2. false
3. true
4. false
5. true
6. false
7. false
8. true
9. true
10. false

II.

1. same
2. different
3. different
4. same
5. different
6. same
7. same
8. different
9. same
10. different

III.

1. c
2. b
3. a
4. b
5. b
6. a
7. b
8. b
9. a
10. a

IV.

1. b
2. c
3. a
4. b
5. b
6. b
7. a
8. c

9. a
10. c

V.

1. d
2. a
3. e
4. b
5. c
6. d
7. a
8. b
9. b
10. e

LESSON 6

A.

1. false
2. false
3. false
4. true
5. true

B.

1. definition
2. restatement
3. example
4. restatement
5. definition
6. restatement
7. example
8. restatement
9. definition
10. example

C.

1. that is
2. such as
3. is called
4. in other words

5. such
6. or
7. that is
8. what this means
9. to put it another way
10. especially

D.

1. that is
2. refers to
3. or
4. such as
5. for example
6. consists of
7. like
8. in other words
9. what this means
10. such as

E.

1. no
2. yes
3. no
4. yes
5. no
6. yes
7. yes
8. no
9. no
10. yes

F.

1. a. true
    b. false
2. a. false
    b. true
3. a. true
    b. false
4. a. false
    b. true
5. a. true
    b. true

LESSON 7

A.

1. contrast
2. contrast
3. effect
4. time
5. contrast
6. time
7. contrast
8. effect
9. contrast
10. contrast

B.

1. before   earlier
2. accordingly   effect
3. until   earlier
4. for   cause
5. meanwhile   during
6. since   cause
7. finally   later
8. whenever   during
9. then   later
10. as a result   effect
11. so that   effect
12. while   during
13. whenever   during
14. consequently   effect
15. when   during
16. after   later
17. since   later
18. while   during
19. before   earlier
20. as a consequence   effect

C.

1. contrast
2. cause
3. contrast
4. contrast
5. effect
6. cause
7. effect
8. contrast
9. contrast
10. contrast

D.

1. c
2. c
3. a
4. c
5. b
6. c
7. b
8. c
9. b
10. c

LESSON 8

A.

1. a deputy sheriff
2. a thick, woolen cloth somewhat like felt
3. Feeding on tuna and other large fish
4. To keep foods from spoiling
5. having set fire to three buildings in the town

B.

1. b
2. c
3. a
4. b
5. c
6. b
7. a
8. c
9. c
10. a

C.

1. c
2. a
3. b
4. b
5. a

LESSON 9

A.

1. sounds
2. schedule
3. computer
4. different
5. opportunities

B.

1. a. uncertain
   b. hazardous
   c. unhealthy
   d. unsure
2. a. bold program
   b. courageous exploration
   c. daring venture
   d. undertakes research
3. a. sums not taxed
   b. subtract
   c. deduct
   d. take out
4. a. law forbids it
   b. break the law
   c. failed to do what the law requires
   d. against the law
   e. violation of the law

LESSON 10

I.

1. example
2. definition
3. restatement
4. example
5. example
6. definition
7. restatement
8. definition
9. example
10. restatement

II.

1. contrast
2. time
3. effect
4. cause
5. effect
6. contrast
7. time
8. contrast
9. effect
10. time

III.

1. or
2. that is
3. is called
4. such as
5. in other words
6. like
7. especially
8. for example
9. such as
10. what this means

IV.

1. a
2. c
3. c
4. c
5. a

V.

1. a. false

b. true
c. true
d. true
2. a. true
b. false
c. true
d. false
e. false
3. a. false
b. true
c. false
d. false
e. true
4. a. false
b. false
c. true
d. true
e. false
5. a. false
b. true
c. false
d. true

LESSON 11

A.

1. outside
2. between, among
3. self
4. too much
5. within
6. many
7. wrong
8. before
9. bad
10. small

B.

1. earth
2. device for measuring
3. study or science
4. distant
5. life
6. light
7. false
8. small
9. sound
10. device for seeing or observing

C.

1. small
2. observe
3. life
4. light
5. earth
6. false
7. life
8. device for measuring
9. distant
10. sound

D.

1. wrong
2. bad
3. too much
4. many
5. before
6. within
7. between, among
8. outside
9. before
10. self

E.

1. later
2. extremely
3. too
4. outside
5. small
6. before
7. within
8. many
9. bad
10. himself

LESSON 12

A.

1. yes
2. no
3. yes
4. yes
5. no
6. yes
7. yes
8. no
9. yes
10. yes

B.

1. yes
2. no
3. no
4. yes
5. yes
6. yes
7. yes
8. yes
9. yes
10. yes

C.

1. within
2. within
3. not
4. within
5. not
6. not
7. within
8. not
9. not
10. not
11. within
12. within

D.

1. opposite
2. opposite
3. away
4. away
5. opposite
6. not
7. opposite
8. not
9. not
10. away

E.

1. back
2. again
3. again
4. back
5. back
6. out
7. former
8. out
9. former
10. against
11. curing
12. preventing
13. against
14. preventing
15. twice
16. partly, somewhat
17. partly, somewhat
18. beneath, below
19. less than
20. beneath, below

F.

1. il
2. un
3. in
4. un
5. dis
6. un
7. un
8. un
9. im
10. in
11. dis
12. in
13. il
14. dis
15. un
16. un
17. un
18. in
19. un
20. in

LESSON 13

A.

1. majority
2. acquaintance
3. broiler
4. error
5. infection
6. failure
7. security
8. adornment
9. allowance
10. frequency
11. conference
12. exposure
13. astonishment
14. annoyance
15. agreement
16. insistence
17. arrival
18. prevention
19. entirety
20. darkness

B.

1. generalize
2. testify
3. elevate
4. notify
5. lengthen
6. commercialize
7. gratify
8. magnetize
9. terrify
10. terrorize
11. hearten
12. mystify
13. strengthen
14. authorize
15. illustrate
16. solidify
17. tenderize
18. lighten
19. eliminate
20. threaten

C.

1. yearly
2. golden
3. marvelous
4. bookish
5. assertive
6. formal
7. likely
8. perilous
9. national
10. persistent
11. dusty
12. outlandish
13. confident
14. collective
15. friendly
16. childish
17. lovely
18. additional
19. effective
20. windy

D.

1. friendly
2. straighten
3. disturbance
4. different
5. feverish
6. announcement
7. neighborly
8. alertness
9. suggestion
10. specialize
11. entertainment
12. dangerous
13. greatness
14. weakness
15. realize

LESSON 14

A.

1. decorate
2. decide
3. please
4. create
5. approve
6. try
7. mystery
8. apology
9. spice
10. carry

B.

1. exclaim
2. single
3. grade
4. prevail
5. inscribe
6. contend
7. provide
8. malice
9. race
10. commit
11. deceive
12. maintain
13. retain
14. miracle
15. frequent
16. conclude
17. submit
18. perceive
19. liable
20. obstinate

C.

1. factual
2. intellectual
3. contractual
4. detention
5. muscular
6. extension
7. frequency
8. revelation
9. conception
10. provision
11. collision
12. remission
13. suspension
14. availability
15. sustenance
16. financial
17. retention
18. absorption
19. accuracy
20. ministry

D.

1. hands
2. hand
3. heard
4. good
5. end
6. body
7. steps
8. deaths
9. end
10. dead
11. body
12. earth
13. faith
14. believe
15. drawn
16. look after
17. throw or place
18. draw or pull
19. bring
20. drives

E.

1. b
2. c
3. a
4. b
5. c

LESSON 15

I.

1. d
2. i
3. g
4. j
5. c
6. b
7. e

8. h
9. a
10. f

II.

1. life
2. earth
3. sounds
4. distance
5. small
6. measure
7. seeing
8. study
9. light
10. false

III.

1. bad
2. small
3. many
4. outside
5. later
6. wrong
7. before
8. before
9. self
10. not
11. too much
12. within
13. between
14. beyond

IV.

1. preventing
2. not
3. inside
4. not
5. against
6. twice
7. before
8. below
9. somewhat
10. not

11. less than
12. not
13. not
14. opposite
15. not
16. not
17. opposite
18. inside
19. opposite
20. opposite

V.

1. renewal
2. identity
3. failure
4. childish
5. magical
6. elective
7. mysterious
8. soften
9. notify
10. specialize

VI.

1. maintenance
2. perception
3. division
4. recency
5. commercial
6. muscular
7. liability
8. hungry
9. attention
10. commission

VII.

1. hand
2. hear
3. believe
4. good
5. faith
6. place
7. draw

8. body
9. end
10. look after
11. end
12. earth
13. drive *or* beat
14. throw
15. step
16. bring
17. draw
18. death
19. faith
20. drive

VIII.

1. real
2. continue
3. value
4. cred
5. system
6. tract
7. mature
8. respond *or* response
9. history
10. forest

MIDWAY CHECK

I.

1. such as
2. means
3. especially
4. copper, gold, and silver coins
5. moving from one part of the country to another
6. that is
7. in which a small portion of a substance placed in a flame burns with a distinctive color
8. taking temperatures, blood pressures, and pulse rates
9. the age at which they have full rights and responsibilities of an adult
10. that is

II.

1. <u>although</u>   contrast
2. <u>accordingly</u>   effect

184

3. <u>when</u>   time

4. <u>nonetheless</u>   contrast

5. <u>since</u>   cause

6. <u>while</u>   contrast

7. <u>yet</u>   contrast

8. <u>since</u>   time

9. <u>however</u>   contrast

10. <u>because</u>   cause

III.

1. a
2. c
3. b
4. c
5. b
6. a
7. c
8. b
9. a
10. b

IV.

1. b
2. c
3. c
4. a

V.

1. not
2. back
3. small
4. device for measuring
5. distant
6. false
7. bad
8. wrong
9. opposite
10. study of
11. outside
12. within
13. inside *or* within
14. too much
15. preventing

16. opposite

17. inside *or* within

18. away

19. again

20. twice

21. less than

22. out

23. below

24. beyond

VI.

1. nomination
2. childish
3. departure
4. acquaintance
5. brighten
6. terrorize
7. nationality
8. solidify
9. attractive
10. quickness

VII.

1. respond
2. permit
3. effect
4. migrate
5. modern
6. necessity
7. orchestra
8. reveal
9. system
10. term
11. suggest
12. pretend
13. real
14. press

LESSON 16

A.

1. no
2. no
3. no
4. yes
5. no
6. yes
7. yes
8. no
9. yes
10. yes
11. no
12. no
13. yes
14. no
15. no
16. yes
17. no
18. no
19. no
20. no

B.

1. yes
2. no
3. no
4. yes
5. yes
6. no
7. yes
8. yes
9. yes
10. no
11. yes
12. no
13. yes
14. no
15. yes
16. yes
17. no
18. no
19. yes
20. yes

C.

1. b
2. a
3. c
4. c
5. c
6. b
7. c
8. a
9. c
10. a
11. b
12. c
13. a
14. c
15. c

D.

1. e
2. f
3. h
4. j
5. i
6. c
7. b
8. g
9. d
10. a

LESSON 17

A.

1. L
2. F
3. F
4. F
5. F
6. F
7. L
8. F
9. L
10. F
11. L
12. L
13. F
14. L
15. F
16. F
17. F
18. F

19. F
20. L

B.

1. F
2. L
3. F
4. F
5. F
6. F
7. L
8. F
9. L
10. F
11. F
12. L
13. L
14. F
15. F
16. F
17. L
18. F
19. L
20. F

C.

1. reifying
2. reifying
3. personifying
4. exaggeration
5. reifying
6. personifying
7. personifying
8. personifying
9. personifying
10. exaggeration
11. personifying
12. lying
13. lying
14. lying
15. exaggeration
16. exaggeration
17. personifying
18. exaggeration
19. reifying
20. reifying

LESSON 18

A.

1. a. true
   b. false
   c. true
2. a. false
   b. false
   c. true
3. a. false
   b. true
   c. true

B.

1. a. false
   b. true
   c. true
2. a. false
   b. true
   c. true
   d. true
3. a. false
   b. true
   c. false

LESSON 19

A.

1. inform
   get to do
2. inform
   get to do
3. amuse
   get to do
4. inform
   express feelings
5. get to believe
   get to do

B.

1. inform
   get to do
2. inform
   get to believe

3. inform
   get to do
4. inform
   express feelings
5. arouse feelings
   get to do

LESSON 20

A.

1. yes
2. yes
3. no
4. no
5. yes
6. yes
7. yes
8. yes
9. no
10. no

B.

1. most important
   assistant
2. committee
   question
3. senators
   disagree
4. promises
   prevent
5. entertain
   conference
6. signs
   agreement
7. considers
   limit
8. makes public
   disagreement

C.

1. increased
2. to investigate
3. candidates
4. to present

5. to hinder or prevent
6. to move ahead
7. to cut
8. to present or put on
9. a campaign
10. to choose

D.

1. c
2. a
3. b
4. c
5. a
6. b
7. b
8. a
9. b
10. c

E.

1. b
2. b
3. c
4. c
5. b

LESSON 21

I.

1. yes
2. no
3. no
4. yes
5. no
6. no
7. no
8. yes
9. no
10. yes

II.

1. a

186

2. b
3. c
4. b
5. b
6. a
7. a
8. b
9. a
10. b

III.

1. L
2. F
3. L
4. F
5. F
6. F
7. F
8. L
9. F
10. F
11. F
12. F
13. L
14. F
15. L

IV.

1. a. false
   b. false
   c. true
2. a. true
   b. false
   c. true
   d. false

V.

1. a. to amuse
   b. to get someone to
      believe something
2. a. to arouse feelings
   b. to get someone to
      do something

VI.

1. question
2. committee
3. investigate
4. oppose or prevent
5. consider
6. examine
7. fight or disagree
8. promise or assure
9. limit or halt
10. delay

VII.

1. no
2. yes
3. yes
4. no
5. no
6. no
7. yes
8. yes
9. no
10. yes

LESSON 22

A.

1.
   (1) example
   (2) example
   (3) example
2.
   (1) added
   (2) added
3.
   (1) added
   (2) explanation
   (3) added
   (4) explanation
4.
   (1) example
   (2) example
   (3) added

5.
   (1) explanation
   (2) example
   (3) added

B.

1.
   (1) explanation
   (2) example
   (3) added
2.
   (1) explanation
   (2) example
   (3) added
   (4) added
3.
   (1) example
   (2) added
   (3) added

LESSON 23

A.

1. This was to be...broken.
   explanation
2. All four flyers survived the mishap.
   detail
3. The monarch is distinguished...black.
   explanation

B.

1. summary
2. example
3. detail

C.

1. summary
2. time
3. time
4. detail
5. example
6. detail

187

LESSON 24

A.

1. 5
2. 1 and 2
3. 6
4. 4
5. 3

B.

1. the writer's
2. Miles Milanovich
3. Chess fans
4. No
5. Svetozar Gligoric

C.

1. 1
2. 3
3. 2

D.

1. 1

2. 2 and 3
3. 4 and 5

E.

1. others
2. writer
3. writer
4. others
5. others
6. writer
7. writer
8. others

LESSON 25

A.

1. no
2. no
3. yes
4. no
5. yes

B.

1. no

2. yes
3. no
4. no
5. yes

C.

1. yes
2. no
3. no
4. no
5. yes

LESSON 26

A.

1. 1421 W. Lake
2. 753-4290
3. 765-7165
4. 146 Broadway
5. 243-8824
6. 142 3 Av

B.

1. United States
   Government

2. after
3. after
4. before

C.

1. yes
2. yes
3. yes
4. no
5. no
6. yes
7. no
8. no

D.

1. no
2. no
3. no
4. yes
5. no